The World Copper Market: An Economic Analysis

The World Copper Market: An Economic Analysis

Ferdinand E. Banks

Associate Professor and Research Fellow
The University of Uppsala (Sweden)

Ballinger Publishing Company ● **Cambridge, Mass.**
A Subsidiary of J. B. Lippincott Company

Library of Congress Catalog Card Number: 73–16165

International Standard Book Number: 0–88410–257–2

Printed in the United States of America

Library of Congress Cataloging in Publication Data

Banks, Ferdinand E
   The world copper market.

1. Copper trade and industry.   I. Title.
HD9539.C6B35   382'.42'43   73–16165
ISBN 0–88410–257–2

Dedication

To my parents

Table of Contents

List of Figures and Tables

Preface

     I began thinking about writing this book while working with Alfred Maizels at the United Nations Conference on Trade and Development (UNCTAD) in Geneva. At the time I was occupied with commodities such as zinc, aluminum, rubber, etc., but for some reason copper seemed to get the majority of attention.

     Eventually I produced a memorandum which could only be called a distinguished example of econometric and algebraic overkill. It also suffered from containing an unusually large number of mistakes. However, in subsequent discussions with various colleagues, I came to the conclusion that most of my difficulty originated from a misunderstanding of the complexity of the copper market—it is *not* complex at all; and in addition, I was guilty of an erroneous vision of the part that econometrics and other advanced quantitative methods should play in the analysis of this market: these devices should at all times be subordinate to economic theory.

     The result of this rather delayed enlightenment is the present study. I hardly think it free of fault, but I have no doubt that much of it can be read without great effort, and that most readers should leave the first few chapters with a reasonable insight into the way in which the copper market functions. In addition, I hope that the structure and content of this book can serve as a guide to investigators interested in other commodities.

     With one exception (the last section of Chapter 1) I have tried to keep mathematics out of the main body of the text in the first six chapters. I would strongly advise, however, that all readers with an elementary smattering of economics examine Appendix A. During the discussion of the penultimate draft of this book at the Higher Seminar for Economic Analysis at the University of Uppsala, there was an unfortunate tendency to organize thinking about this market around the simple flow model. This is not completely wrong, but it is more wrong than right, and in this Appendix I try to introduce the reader to the correct model.

     The last two chapters consist of some econometric materials. I wish

I could say that these chapters are for specialists, but in truth they are quite tame. I am, however, satisfied with them as far as they go, and I felt it unnecessary to go farther since about the time I was making plans to extend this material, Fisher, Cootner, and Baily published their article, "An Econometric Model of the World Copper Industry" (1972). This important paper says about as much on the subject of commodity econometrics as it is possible to say at the present time, and I strongly recommend it to all commodity economists about to set off for the econometric wars.

Some question, of course, will always come up about the possibility of getting price forecasts from econometric models. I don't think there is much question that some reasonable ceteris paribus projections are possible if enough trends can be fed into such a model. By ceteris paribus I mean forecasts that depend upon the environment remaining the same: no strikes, revolutions, large new deposits exploited, changes in taste, etc. But as for the possibility of getting something that can be used outside the seminar room, I can only refer to the *question* I reply with when my students ask me if *I* am prepared to accept and use forecasts of commodity prices from models developed by competent and responsible econometricians. My question is, "If I were at the Museum Club in Stockholm, and the Abominable Snowman asked me to dance with him, would I accept?" The answer is yes, because I don't expect to encounter the Abominable Snowman in the first place, and if I did I hardly think he would regard me as a suitable dancing partner. Besides, the Museum Club is in Montreux.

At this point I would like to thank a number of individuals and organizations for assisting me, in one way or another, with this work. First of all *Statens Råd för Samhällsforskning* for a grant which enabled me to track down a great deal of material that appeared after I left UNCTAD, and without whose assistance this book could not have been written.

I also owe an important debt to my former colleagues at UNCTAD. In particular I must mention Walter Labys, now of the University of Geneva; and A. Megzari whose memorandum "Cuivre" gave me a few hints into how some of my work should be organized. I would also like to thank Dennis Pike, Alan Lamond, and Brian Chambers of the UNCTAD Commodities Division, the librarians of the ECE–UNCTAD Reference Room, and of course P.B.W. Rayment, formerly with UNCTAD, and now Editor of the Economic Survey of the Economic Commission for Europe (ECE).

I am also indebted to Kenji Takeuchi of the World Bank, Per Eklund of Uppsala University and World Bank, Jacques Da of the Intergovernmental Council of Copper Exporting Countries (CIPEC), Göran Phillipsson of Grängesberg AB., and various economists of the Batelle Institute (Geneva) and UNIDO (Vienna). Finally, I would like to mention my present colleagues, Professors Ohlin and Bentzel, and to thank them for the warm encouragement they have given me to complete this book.

Ferdinand E. Banks

Acknowledgments

The following acknowledgements are in order: to Claes Brundenius and the *Journal of Peace Research* for permission to reproduce portions of his article, "The Anatomy of Imperialism: Multinational Mining in Peru." To Kenji Takeuchi and the *Developing Economies* for permission to reproduce portions of his article, "CIPEC and the Copper Export Earnings of Member Countries." To the United Nations Industrial Development Organization for permission to use material from "Economic Aspects of Copper Production and Marketing Possibilities for Developing Countries" by G.S. Somerset, and "Opportunities in the Production of Secondary Non Ferrous Metals" by Max. J. Spendlove. To the General Agreement on Tariffs and Trade for permission to quote from "Import Duties on Copper and Copper Products," COM.TD/71. To Springer–Verlag, Vienna, for permission to use material from my article, "An Econometric Note on the Demand for Refined Zinc"; to the *Ekonomiska Samfundets Tidskrift* for permission to use material from my article, "The Economics of Exhaustible Resources: A Note"; to the *Schweizerische Zeitschrift für Volkswirtschaft und Statistik* for permission to reprint a part of my article, "A Diagramatic Presentation of Dynamic Supply Behavior; to the *Malayan Economic Review* for permission to use material from my article, "The Optimal Conditions in a Surplus Labor Economy"; to the *Pakistan Development Review* for permission to use a part of my article, "Capital Allocation and the Real Cost of Labour," and to UNCTAD for permission to use UNCTAD reference materials.

The World Copper Market:
An Economic Analysis

Chapter One

Background and Introduction

This is a book in applied economics. Its purpose is to give the reader a more or less complete insight into the functioning of the world copper market. As will soon be observed, this is an uncomplicated but time-consuming job, since there are many topics to cover. Therefore, this chapter will serve to survey and introduce the subject.

Perhaps the best way to begin is to consider, in broad outline, some aspects of the technical structure of the copper industry. The production of copper moves from the mining stage, to stages where the ore is "milled," "smelted," and "refined," right through to a stage where the output of the refinery (which is almost pure copper) is turned by a fabricator into what are known as semi-fabricates or "semis." The form for these semis is sheets, tubes, rods, and wires. The next step is to turn the semis into such things as components for plumbing and heating installations, where these components (such as cables, fixtures, etc.) are called "end uses." The situation with regard to all these operations is summed up in Figure 1–1.

The first important operation in the cycle shown in Figure 1–1 is the mining. This produces a copper containing ore with a content of less than 6 percent, and for the most part much less. One of the most modern installations in the world is now coming into operation on Bougainville Island, in the territory of Papua and New Guinea, and it has a grade of about 0.49 percent. In order to produce 150,000 tons of copper per year, 30 million tons of ore (150,000/0.0049) must be mined and treated.

The next stage is often called milling. First the ore is crushed and ground to obtain a powder, and this is then "concentrated" in order to separate the copper and other metals. The concentrate averages about 30 percent copper.

Next comes smelting, which first calls for roasting to remove sulphur, followed by the smelting proper. This produces a "matte" containing about

Figure 1–1. Flow Chart of the Copper Industry for a Typical Industrial Country

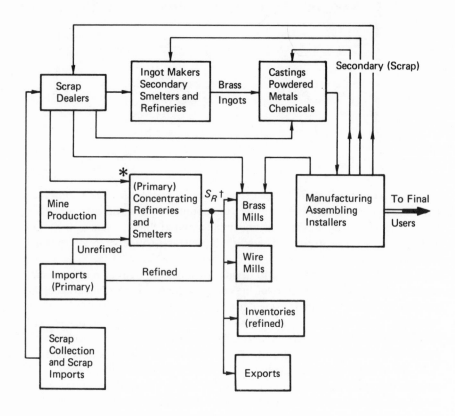

Source: U.S. government publications.
*Some scrap is treated in primary processes.
†S_R = Supply of Refined.

32 percent copper; this process is followed by converting the matte into "blister" copper which has about a 99 percent purity.

The last stage calls for turning the blister into refined copper. The first operation here is usually fire refining, and this gives a copper which can be used directly by some fabricators. Most of this copper, however, is subsequently electrolytically refined, especially that which is to be used in electric conductors. Refined copper is almost 100 percent pure.

It should be noted that the weight of the foregoing discussion has fallen on so-called primary copper, which is copper that has gone through the cycle mining-smelting-refining one time and is ready for movement to brass mills, wire mills, etc., where it is rolled, drawn, and extruded into semi-fabricates.

On the other hand, an important source of copper is provided by what is known as secondary copper, which is also called scrap. Secondary copper comes either from the reduction of finished goods containing copper (such as pipes, cables, etc.) or from the fabrication process itself (in the form of shavings, etc.). Forty percent of the total copper consumption (refined metal and copper base alloys) of the nonsocialist world has its origin in scrap, and the secondary copper industry is the largest of the secondary nonferrous metals industries.

Copper is alloyed with zinc and tin to make brass and bronze—probably the best known of the many copper alloys; and a large part of the input of brass mills consists of unprocessed old and new scrap. This last point is important! What it means is that secondary copper can be divided into two categories. The first is that portion of scrap that goes, sometimes via earlier processing, through the refinery. This is called secondary *refined*. (In the U.S. in 1965 this amounted to 403,000 metric tons.) The other category, comprised of various grades of scrap, is used for such things as inputs for brass mills. (In the U.S. in 1965 this category came to 775,000 metric tons.) It is interesting to note that much copper mined in the last 100 years is still available for use today. The scrap recovery percentage averages out at 75 percent, with the recovery percentage for copper used in heavy electrical conductors standing at about 90 percent. On the other side, the destructive uses of copper are decreasing over time, and it seems to be the case that strong political and economic pressures are building up that will cause an increase in the percentage of copper being recycled.

Today in France, India, and the U.S.S.R. legislation exists that prevents copper from being imported for use in applications where aluminum would suffice. It has been said that if this sort of legislation were introduced in other countries, it would probably liberate such a large amount of scrap that a drastic reduction in the demand for primary copper would occur.

The principal shape in which refined unwrought copper is traded is the wirebar. This has a trapezium shape, is between 38 and 54 inches in length, and weighs 135 to 420 pounds. On the LME electrolytic copper in the weight range of 200 to 275 pounds, in the form of wirebars, is traded.

The shape most commonly used for the casting of fire refined copper is the ingot, or ingot bar. It is also the shape most commonly used for copper alloys made from secondary materials by ingot makers. The usual weight for ingots is between 20 and 35 pounds, while ingot bars usually weigh between 50 and 70 pounds.

Finally, the cathode is the flat plate that is produced by electrolytic refining.

CONSUMPTION AND PRODUCTION

Table 1–1 shows the major contributors to consumption and production, the growth rate of consumption for the major consumers, and the distribution of imports among some of the major consumers.

Among other things, this table indicates that a large part of mined copper originates in the less developed countries, and that all but negligible consumption takes place in the industrialized nations. The pattern of ownership, of course, is much more complicated, and this will be taken up to a considerable extent in the following chapter. It can be stated right now, however, that as a commodity of major importance to the less developed countries, copper must be ranked right behind oil, rubber, and coffee, and about on the same level as cocoa, cotton, tin, and tea. The imports of copper into the major consumers among the market economy industrial countries, from the less developed countries, amounted to approximately 2,2 billions of American dollars in 1968. Of the world's copper production, about 40 percent takes place in the less developed countries, with activity centering on Chile, Peru, Zambia, Zaire (Congo), the Phillipines, and Bougainville. Table 1–2 takes up some aspects of the first four countries (the ones belonging to the Intergovernmental Council of Copper Exporting Countries [CIPEC]).

Peru's situation may appear unspectacular, but it so happens that in value terms, copper exports by far outpace the general export trend. It also is the case that these figures, while of some interest, actually understate the importance of copper (and other commodities) exports to the less developed countries. As we know, in most of these countries income tax rates are usually quite low. Thus, a key source of revenue is the tax on imports, particularly imports of consumption goods. What we see in Table 1–2 is the direct component of government revenue—that resulting from profit taxes, export taxes, licenses, and certain types of indirect levies. At the same time it should be recognized that other taxes derive from an activity such as copper production. (An example here might be a profit or indirect tax on the railroad that moves this copper to the next stage of processing or to a port.) The aforementioned tax on imports is taken as being especially important in this context, since with the exports of a particular commodity being a sizable percentage of *all* exports, it usually is the case that imports are also a direct and uncomplicated function of these exports. Larger exports thus mean larger tax revenues, since the income from this enlarged export production spills over into increased imports due to the underdevelopment of import-competing industries. The next step is to get some idea of the development of copper production and capacity over a fairly normal period. This development is shown in Table 1–3.

As far as I have been able to find out, the normal operating rate (= mining capacity utilization) is regarded to be about 92 percent. In 1956 and

Table 1-1. Mine Production and Refined Consumption* (1971) and Imports (by Percents)

Mine Production (1971) Major Producers		Major Consumers	Refined Consumption (1971)†	Major Importers (% of Total)	Percentage Copper 1971-72	Growth Rate Consumption (1961-70)
Zaire	406	U.S.A.	1,829 (26%)	9	9.2	3.3
Zambia	651	U.S.S.R.	1,030 (14%)	0.5		
S. Africa	148	Japan	826 (11%)	21	14.2	8.1
Australia	175	W. Germany	631 (9%)	15	6.3	2.2
Phillipines	197	U.K.	509 (7%)	11	2.4	-0.4
Bougainville ‡	124	France	343 (5%)	9	4.4	3.2
Chile	708	Italy	270 (4%)	7	-1.9	3.1
Peru	212	Spain	103 (1.4%)		17.0	7.0
U.S.A.	1380	Holland	42 (0.5%)			
Canada	653	Brazil	60 (0.8%)		5.0	4.5
		Mexico	60 (0.8%)		8.3	10.4
		Belgium	113 (1.6%)		9.1	1.5
		Sweden	91 (1.3%)			

Source: Various publications (World Bureau of Metal Statistics, and Metallgesellschaft).
*Production and consumption in thousands of tons.
† Percentage of total world consumption in parenthesis.
‡Estimated for 1972.

Table 1-2. Miscellaneous Data: CIPEC Countries

Country	GNP Per Capita (1970)*	Copper Share in GDP (1968)	Manufacturing Industry Share in GNP (1970)	Copper Exports as % of Total Exports (1970)	% of Govt. Revenue from Copper (1968)
Zambia	405	46	11	93	68
Zaire	109	18	6	61	45
Chile	794	6	29	66	14
Peru	430	7	21	19	12.5

Source: U.N. Yearbook of World Trade and U.N. Yearbook of National Account Stat.   *In dollars.

Table 1–3. Miscellaneous Statistics: Mining Capacity, Total World Production and Consumption of Refined Copper, U.S. Strategic Stocks

Year	Mining Capacity Utilization	World Production Refined	World Consumption Refined	Surplus (%)	Estimated U.S. Strategic Stocks
1956	101.4				884,300
1957	90.2				931,800
1958	86.9				1,011,400
1959	88.5				1,136,100
1960	94.9				1,140,600
1961	92.4				1,146,600
1962	93.0				1,134,200
1963	92.4				1,122,800
1964	92.4				1,095,500
1965	93.9				910,200
1966	95.0				459,600
1967	84.4	5,995	6,155	−2.5	282,200
1968	90.2	6,655	6,442	3.2	268,500
1969		7,172	7,062	1.5	
1970		7,543	7,176	4.8	
1971		7,339	7,220	1.6	
1972		7,847	7,731	1.5	

Source: World Metal Statistics, Metallgesellschaft, CIPEC Quarterly Reports, and U.S. Government Stockpile Reports.

Notes: Refined production and consumption for market economies and centrally planned economies, in 000's of metric tons; strategic stocks in short tons. Mining capacity utilization in Percents.

1957, however, this was up to 101.4 and 96.2, respectively. I have no definite information on how this first figure was achieved, but under normal circumstances it would probably mean an unusually large increase in the variable factors of production—principally labor—and considerable overtime.

Figures for the U.S. Strategic Stockpile (or National Stockpile) have also been estimated. There is a so-called *official* level at which the stockpile is supposed to be maintained (and which is said to be 750,000 tons); however, there is some problem in explaining how the stockpile will act as a reserve for wartime, stabilize prices in the U.S., *and* be operated without substantial financial losses if this official level is to be respected.

More on the topic of stockpiles will be discussed later, but it should be pointed out that the U.S. Stockpile undoubtedly prevented copper prices from increasing beyond the record heights attained during the Vietnam War—favoring American consumers in particular, but also making its presence felt in Europe.

A BRIEF HISTORY

The history of copper goes back about 4,000 years (although experts say that man's familiarity with copper can be traced back 9,000 years). In particular, an extensive trade in copper between Africa and the Eastern Mediterranean seems to have gone on since the dawn of antiquity; while in Japan, for example, the mining of copper dates back to the Bronze Age. About the year 1500 the merchant Jacob Fugger was able to gain control of the mines of Hungary and the Tyrol, at that time the world's chief source of copper; and 300 years later the center of gravity of world copper production shifted to Sweden and the mines at Stora Kopparberg. Later, toward the end of the 18th century and the early years of the industrial revolution, English exports from Cornwall dominated world trade in this commodity.

It was in the late 1880s that the pattern of organization of the world market for copper took a sharp change. The reason for this, quite simply, was that due to the acceleration of industrialization the demand for copper climbed to record heights, and suddenly the copper market became a place where a great deal of money could be made.

Among the first to grasp this highly significant fact, while at the same time being in position to take advantage of it, was the French financier Pierre Secretan. What this gentleman did was to organize a syndicate whose express purpose was the manipulating of the world copper price in such a manner as to guarantee himself and his colleagues profits on a scale previously unheard of in the mineral industries. Supported by the French banks they were able to secure, by contracting for copper on a fixed price basis, what amounted to a corner on the market. On the London Metal Exchange the price rose in a few months from about 40 pounds per ton to 80 pounds. Enormous inventories of copper were accumulated, and profits were made both in the metal itself and in mining shares.

But as the case would be time and again in the future, the high price of copper stimulated production to a point where substantial supplies of copper began to flow onto the market. The syndicate found itself having to purchase more than ever in order to maintain its corner, and at the same time the London Metal Exchange, which previously had dealt only in what was called Chile Bars, expanded its operations to include so-called Good Merchantable Brands. In 1889 the inevitable happened. One of the banks supporting Monsieur Secretan went bankrupt, and the others began to lose their nerve when faced with the amount of copper it was necessary to buy in order to continue holding up the price. When they changed their strategy to sell instead of buy, the price immediately fell by one-half, and the Secretan escapade was over.

As far as the general public knows, this was the last attempt made by a nonmining person or group to control the price of copper. Thereafter producers—or, more correctly, groups of producers or cartels—took over this task. Perhaps the first attempt along these lines occurred in 1892 when the American Producers' Association agreed to hold production for the year 1892–93 to less than 140,000 and to keep exports below 40,000 tons. For their part of the deal, European producers were to reduce output by 15 percent, a figure to which they did not agree. Instead the Europeans reduced production by 5 percent, and after adjustments had been made by the Americans, the price was only affected by a trivial amount.

A stronger cartel was formed about the turn of the century. The key company involved was Standard Oil (which included the Anaconda Corporation among its subordinates); and by a judicious strategy of buying on the market and restricting production, it was possible to raise the price of copper from 11–13 cents to 17–18 cents per pound. Plans were made for further increases, but producers outside the U.S. declined to cooperate. Not only that, but given the increased price of copper they increased production. Under the circumstances, the cartels' output restriction policies came to a rapid conclusion.

The next venture along these lines came in 1918. Assisted by the Webb-Pomerane Act of 10 April, 1918 (which permitted the operation of American cartels in foreign, but not domestic, markets), a cartel known as the Copper Export Association came into being. This group was able to realize some success in its output restrictive policies until 1923, when it broke down due to the inability of its members to cooperate. Just what effect this particular cartel had on the domestic price of copper is uncertain, but there is no question about its ability to influence the export price.

In 1926 a stronger organization, Copper Exporters, Inc. (CEI), was formed. This cartel included foreign as well as American producers, and it was estimated that they controlled 85 percent of the world's copper production. Under agreements reached by this group, prices outside the U.S. were to be fixed by committees meeting in Brussels and New York, and it took only a few years to get the price up to 25 cents per pound (although, it should be noted, the cartel was operating in a period of rising prices).

Given the technological progress being made in the mining industry at this time, a price of 25 cents per pound was dangerous for the cartel. What it did was to encourage an expansion of production by producers outside the cartel, putting a downward pressure on prices that intensified as the great depression set in. Further price restrictions were agreed on, but the avalanche was under way. At this point all earlier agreements were discarded, and to the cry of every man for himself, producers began a general round of price undercutting and other ungentlemanly practices. Eventually the price reached 5 cents per pound, but by this time the CEI was on its way to becoming a memory.

In 1932 the U.S. government imposed a tariff of 4 cents per pound on copper, thereby turning the American market completely over to domestic producers. Unfortunately, however, the economic situation as a whole could not be treated with similar medicine, and an extremely depressed state of world demand kept mining activity in the U.S. at an all-time low. In 1935 a sort of optimism swept over the industry, and a new cartel came into being. This was called the International Copper Cartel and included producers from Zambia, the Congo, Chile, and so on. The principle to be applied this time was to impose quotas on producers during periods when the demand was low and to remove them when the price reached a certain level. The quotas were originally for 25 percent of capacity, and these were removed twice (during 1937 and 1938). These occasions were originally termed recoveries, but in truth they were only mild interruptions of the general downturn. It was only when the time came to start tooling up for the second World War that the price of copper resumed what had, in the distant past, been considered normal levels.

During the war years the copper industry operated under full capacity, and although only a modest amount of new investment was initiated, production was increased substantially over pre-war levels. The reason for this was the surplus facilities available from the thirties, as well as the fact that a new generation of technology was exploiting extremely rich deposits. These factors enabled the American copper industry to supply, either directly or indirectly, a large part of the requirements of all the Allied fighting fronts, as well as military and naval construction programs, and to build up impressive stockpiles whose influence on pricing must be taken into consideration right down to the present day.

After the war the U.S. dropped its import duty (which was later re-imposed at a lower level) and became a net importer of copper. This was a period in which the cold war was coming into its own, and among other things this meant that the governments of the U.S. and Western Europe cultivated a strong, if unspoken, determination to exclude from their experience the disruptive and wasteful price and production movements of the thirties. Full employment policies and the Marshall Plan kept the industry working at a high capacity on a worldwide basis, and by 1950 the world copper market was beginning to assume its basic, post-war shape as characterized by a high rate of investment and considerable integration, both vertical (particularly within the U.S.) and horizontal (outside the U.S.).

In 1953 the London Metal Exchange opened after a closure of fourteen years. The price of copper had risen from 60 pounds a ton in 1946 to 250 pounds in 1953; and just before the opening, expectations were that selling from U.S. inventories would force the price down. When the exchange opened the price did, in fact, dip to 215 pounds; but it later recovered to about 240 pounds. The reason for this, quite simply, is that given the institutional structure of the industry, the "freeing" of the market did not take place to the extent expected. The copper industry is, for obvious reasons, a natural oligopoly, and it hardly made good sense to expect the London Metal Exchange to function in the manner of the Chicago Grain Exchange. It must be admitted, however, that as a pricing and hedging market the London Exchange performs an important function. The topic of hedging will be treated later in this book, but where pricing outside the U.S. is concerned, it is quite common to find the price quoted on contracts tied to the London Metal Exchange (LME) price by some sort of formula. In general this sort of arrangement has been acceptable to most categories of producers and consumers, since the feeling is that transactions on the London Exchange, marginal though they may seem in terms of quantity, do in fact reflect the supply-demand situation of the world as a whole.

By 1957 investments initiated in the early 1950s began to reflect on the supply of copper. The price began to fall, and with the onset of a minor recession in the U.S., the London price per ton registered a drop from 435 pounds in 1956 to 160 pounds in 1958. The GATT tariff negotiations, which began in 1947, now proved to be an unfortunate nuisance to American producers, since they prevented the imposition of a tariff of sufficient magnitude to shield the U.S. market from foreign copper. Under the circumstances, American production was forced down. Tariffs fell from 4 cents per pound in 1947 to 1.7 cents per pound in 1956, and in fact these were suspended for the most part. But in 1958 a figure of 1.7 cents per pound became operative and has remained in effect ever since. As the recession in the U.S. deepened, prices and imports continued to fall; and at times the price was so low that even this small tariff assumed more than a symbolic value, permitting American producers to retain a slight advantage over outsiders. In 1957 a decrease in production of 10 percent was announced by the leading African producers, and the price began to creep upward.

As a result of strikes in the U.S. and Chile, prices on the world market were on a definite upward trend just before the end of 1959. Seventy-five percent of American capacity was idle, and under the circumstances only the presence of large stockpiles kept the price from booming. Once the strike was settled, however, prices began to slide again. Some support was available because of the uncertainty generated by the changing political situation in the Congo, but once more the industry had brought home to it a basic fact of life: when operating at full capacity it could supply, with ease, the existing world demand for copper. Once again cutbacks in supply were introduced, principally in Africa, with some production cuts reaching 15 percent. Later, production was also restricted in Chile and Peru, and a certain amount of stockpiling was resorted to, but bad news continued to predominate in the market reports until mid–1962. At this time a combination of supply restriction and price support operations on the London Metal Exchange stabilized the price at around 236 pounds for a period of two years.

Some people have come to regard this supply restriction-price support (or "valorization") experiment as being one of the most successful operations of its type in history. Perhaps it was, but it was not successful for all the participating firms. One of the things that happened during this period was that many producers built up stocks, while consumers, expecting a fall in price, drew down stocks and, as time passed, sold stocks on the open market. Producers thus found themselves absorbing even higher quantities of copper.

Then, in 1964, demand began to edge up; but many producers, sitting on top of unusually large inventories, were not immediately aware of the change. A large number of them, ready to do anything to prevent having to accept larger stockpiles, pounced on contracts specifying a price near or at the one they had been trying to defend on the London market. As bad luck would have it, this price was too low to bring the market into equilibrium, and consumers took everything they could get. The cost to producers of these premature sales can be reckoned in the tens and perhaps hundreds of millions of dollars.

In 1965 there were some minor fluctuations on the various markets, but three factors were about to combine that would send the price of copper to record levels by 1970. These factors were (a) uncertainty over Zambian supplies in 1965–66; (b) the major strike in the U.S. in 1968; and (c) the war in Vietnam, where huge quantities of copper joined 30 billion American dollars per year in one of the most impressive fiascos of the century. At the moment of writing, a new price trend is visible, and it would not appear to be one that producers will compare favorably with the one just past. Barring major strikes, most predictions say that copper will be in oversupply until the end of this decade.

Just what this oversupply will mean in terms of price is difficult to say. In the last chapter of this book I contend that barring strikes and excessive political tumult, it should mean a price of around 50 cents per pound. In fact, it seems to me that the technology of the industry, as it is evolving, may tolerate even lower prices: highly modern installations like the Bougainville operation or the Prieska copper-zinc project in South Africa seem to be prepared to function quite comfortably with a copper price under 50 cents. Also, after examining Table 1–2, it would be difficult for me to imagine copper mines in the less developed countries stopping production until the price was far lower than 50 cents; and one of the aspects of nationalization that many people seem to have missed is that, for political reasons, many of these nationalized mines may have to produce regardless of profitability.

Finally, the place of inflation in all this should not be forgotten. In the period from 1961 to 1964 the average U.S. producer price of copper was about 30 cents, and the LME price about 230 pounds. Since that time there have been extremely large increases in wages, equipment costs, the cost of money capital, and general economic uncertainty. Thus the average price for 1972 of about 51 cents, when properly deflated, would certainly give a price of no more than 40 cents, and perhaps less.

PRICE SERIES IN LONDON AND THE U.S.

The next step is to look at some price series for copper on both the London and American markets. First, for the London market we have the Figures shown in Table 1–4.

Table 1–4.   LME Prices (1908–72) and World Mine Production; Refined Consumption (1950–72)

Year	Highest Price (1)	Lowest Price (2)	Average of (1) and (2)	World Mine Production (Mkt. Econ.)	World Refined Consumption (Mkt. Econ.)
1908	62.223	59.258	63.5 H		
1909	65.035	58.113	61.5		
1910	63.142	57.192	59.9		
1911	63.475	56.483	59.5 L		
1912	81.750	66.058	73.5 H		
1913	77.901	67.369	72.4		
1914	68.500	52.000	60.0 L		
1915	109.500	60.750	86.6		
1916	171.000	109.000	140.0 H		
1917	151.000	121.000	136.0		
1918	137.000	120.000	128.0		
1919	128.000	76.000	102.0 L		
1920	132.000	80.000	105.0 H		
1921	83.500	70.000	76.5		
1922	74.500	62.500	68.5 L		
1923	83.500	63.000	73.0 H		
1924	74.000	64.250	69.0		
1925	72.250	62.500	67.2		
1926	67.750	63.500	65.5		
1927	67.000	59.500	62.8 L		
1928	77.500	66.000	71.5		
1929	112.625	77.250	94.0 H		
1930	84.250	44.250	64.0		
1931	50.625	32.500	41.7		
1932	50.000	27.500	38.7		
1933	44.250	30.750	37.4		
1934	37.500	28.250	32.4 L		
1935	41.500	29.250	35.3		
1936	54.500	38.250	46.2		
1937	81.000	41.500	61.1 H		
1938	54.750	37.000	45.8 L		
1939	54.500	46.500	50.5		
1940	62.500	62.500	62.5		
1941	62.000	62.000	62.0		
1942	62.000	62.000	62.0		
1943	62.000	62.000	62.0		
1944	62.000	62.000	62.0		
1945	62.000	62.000	62.0		
1946	98.000	62.000	80.0		
1947	137.000	117.000	127.0		
1948	140.000	132.000	136.0 H		
1949	153.000	104.000	128.5 L		

Table 1–4. (cont.)

Year	Highest Price (1)	Lowest Price (2)	Average of (1) and (2)	World Mine Production (Mkt. Econ.)	World Refined Consumption (Mkt. Econ.)
1950	202.000	153.000	177.5	2,287	2,610
1951	234.000	202.000	218.0	2,384	2,747
1952	284.000	227.000	257.0 H	2,443	2,807
1953	285.000	214.000	249.5 L	2,459	2,653
1954	310.000	215.000	262.5	2,485	2,859
1955	405.000	289.000	347.0 H	2,731	3,246
1956	437.000	202.000	317.0	3,031	3,323
1957	272.000	176.000	224.0	3,081	3,325
1958	261.000	160.000	211.0 L	2,957	3,348
1959	267.000	209.250	238.0	3,153	3,541
1960	279.000	217.750	248.3 H	3,617	3,844
1961	249.000	216.250	237.1	3,714	4,118
1962	237.000	227.750	232.4 L	3,811	4,130
1963	236.000	231.000	233.5	3,875	4,391
1964	531.000	235.000	283.0	3,997	4,852
1965	570.000	328,000	449.0	4,152	5,003
1966	787.000	355.000	571.0 H	4,315	5,229
1967	598.000	340.000	410.0 L	4,058	4,861
1968	810.000	425.000	515.0	4,418	5,113
1969	734.000	502.000	611.5 H	4,821	5,705
1970			587.0	5,128	5,703
1971			444.4	5,158	5,639
1972			428.0 L	5,606	6,115

Source: World Bureau of Metal Statistics, and Metallgesellschaft (information above only for market economies).

Note: Prices, from 1966–72 are an annual average. Unit for prices: pounds per metric ton; Units for production and consumption: thousands of metric tons.

Using this table as raw material, another table (Table 1–5) can be constructed that emphasizes the cyclic makeup of copper prices.

Table 1–5.   Peak to Peak Price Cycles: London Metal Exchange*

Start	Finish	Length (Years)	Peak Price	Trough Price	Peak Price	Trend
1908	1912	4	63.5	59.5	73.5	up
1912	1916	4	73.5	60.0	140.0	up
1916	1920	4	140.0	102.0	105.0	down
1920	1923	3	105.0	68.5	73.0	down
1923	1929	6	73.0	62.5	94.0	up
1929	1937	8	94.0	32,4	61.1	down
1937	1939	2	61.1	45.8		up
1948	1952	4	136.0	128.5	257.0	up
1952	1955	3	257.0	249.5	347.0	up
1955	1960	5	347.0	211.0	248.3	down
1960	1966	6	248.3	232.4	571.0	up
1966	1969	3	571.0	410.0	611.5	up
1969	?	?	611.5	428.0		?

Trough to Trough Price Cycles: London Metal Exchange*

Start	Finish	Length (Years)	Trough Price	Peak Price	Trough Price	Trend
1911	1914	3	59.5	73.5	60.0	up
1914	1919	5	60.0	140.0	102.0	up
1919	1922	3	102.0	105.0	68.5	down
1922	1927	5	68.5	73.0	62.8	down
1927	1934	7	62.8	94.0	32.4	down
1934	1938	4	32.4	61.1	45.8	up
1949	1953	4	128.5	257.0	249.5	up
1953	1958	5	249.5	347.0	211.0	down
1958	1962	4	211.0	248.3	232.56	up
1962	1967	5	236.56	571.0	410.0	up
1967	1972	5	410.0	611.5	428.0	up

*Price in pounds per metric ton.

These two tables bring out a very simple fact about the copper market: when economic activity is up, the demand for copper is up; and when economic activity is down, the demand is down. Price plays a very small part in influencing demand, particularly long-run demand. Thus, as Monsieur Secretan probably found out, it is possible for a skillful operator to do quite well for himself by playing the "swings" in the market, but it is quite another matter to hold up the price when there is a general downturn in the business cycle. Tables similar to the previous two can also be presented for the United States (see Table 1–6).

Table 1–6. U.S. Domestic Price (1900–72) and World Smelter Production (1908–66)

Year	Highest Price	Lowest Price	Annual Average	World Smelter Production
1900	16.760	15.580	16.19 H	
1901	16.430	13.820	16.11	
1902	12.175	11.053	11.62	
1903	14.454	11.952	13.24 H	
1904	14.661	12.063	12.83 L	
1905	18.328	14.627	15.59	
1906	22.885	17.869	19.28	
1907	25.065	13.163	20.00 H	
1908	14.130	12.598	13.21	764
1909	13.893	12.387	12.98	858
1910	13.620	12.215	12.74	895
1911	13.552	11.989	12.38 L	916
1912	17.508	14.042	16.34 H	1,019
1913	16.488	14.192	15.27	973
1914	14.491	11.739	13.60 L	927
1915	20.133	13.641	17.28	1,078
1916	31.890	23.865	27.20 H	1,392
1917	31.750	23.500	27.18	1,434
1918	26.000	23.500	24.63	1,423
1919	22.319	14.856	18.69	971
1920	18.918	13.188	17.46	982
1921	13.555	11.634	12.50 L	546
1922	14.500	12.250	13.38	1,281
1923	17.125	12.125	14.42 H	1,281
1924	14.750	12.000	13.02 L	1,381
1925	14.875	13.050	14.05 H	1,442
1926	14.275	13.025	13.79	1,482
1927	13.975	12.175	12.92 L	1,526
1928	16.275	13.650	14.57	1,718
1929	23.775	16.500	18.11 H	1,922
1930	17.775	9.275	12.98	1,574
1931	10.275	6.025	8.12	1,350
1932	7.275	4.775	5.55 L	905
1933	8.775	4.775	7.03	1,090
1934	8.775	7.525	8.43	1,271
1935	9.025	7.775	8.65	1,467
1936	11.775	9.025	9.47	1,677
1937	16.775	9.900	13.17 H	2,267
1938	11.025	8.775	10.00 L	1,984
1939	12.275	9.775	10.96	2,180
1940	12.275	10.275	11.30	2,792
1941	11.950	11.775	11.80 H	2,630
1942	11.775	11.775	11.77 L	2,794
1943	11.775	11.775	11.77	2,854
1944	11.775	11.775	11.77	2,648
1945	11.775	11.775	11.77	2,270
1946	19.275	11.775	13.82	1,875
1947	23.300	19.225	20.96	2,367
1948	23.200	21.200	22.04 H	2,459
1949	23.200	15.700	19.20 L	2,493

Table 1–6. (cont.)

Year	Highest Price	Lowest Price	Annual Average	World Smelter Production
1950	24.200	18.200	21.24	2,791
1951	24.200	24.200	24.20	2,918
1952	24.200	24.200	24.20	2,984
1953	30.750	24.200	28.80	3,097
1954	29.700	29.600	29.70	3,164
1955	45.300	29.700	37.49	3,427
1956	47.800	35.375	41.82 H	3,786
1957	35.600	25.425	29.58	3,818
1958	28.825	23.525	25.76	3,698
1959	35.175	28.600	31.19	3,935
1960	34.175	29.600	32.05 H	4,632
1961	30.675	28.600	29.92 L	4,672
1962	30.600	30.600	30.60	4,792
1963	30.600	30.600	30.60	4,921
1964	33.759	30.600	31.96	5,256
1965	37.045	33.600	35.02	5,543
1966	47.200	35.600	36.18	5,544
1967	39.600	36.200	38.23	5,239
1968	42.300	41.700	41.85	5,881
1969	52.800	41.700	47.53	6,283
1970	59.700	52.100	57.70 H	
1971			51.43	
1972			50.62	

Source: World Bureau of Metal Statistics, Metallgesellschaft, and quarterly reports of CIPEC.
Note: Prices are in cents per pound. Production is in thousands of metric tons.

As before, this can be summarized as follows in Table 1–7.

Table 1–7. Peak to Peak Price Cycles: American Market*

Start	Finish	Length (Years)	Peak Price	Trough Price	Peak Price	Trend
1900	1903	3	16.2	11.6	13.2	down
1903	1907	4	13.2	12.8	20.0	up
1907	1912	5	20.0	12.4	16.3	down
1912	1916	4	16.3	13.6	27.2	up
1916	1923	7	27.2	12.5	14.4	down
1923	1925	2	14.4	13.0	14.0	down
1925	1929	4	14.0	12.9	18.1	up
1929	1937	8	18.1	5.6	13.2	down
1937	1948	5	13.2	10.0	22.0	up
1948	1956	8	22.0	19.2	41.8	up
1956	1960	4	41.8	25.8	32.0	down
1960	1966	6	32.0	29.9	36.2	up

Trough to Trough Price Cycles: American Market*

Start	Finish	Length (Years)	Trough Price	Peak Price	Trough Price	Trend
1902	1904	2	11.6	13.2	12.8	up
1904	1911	7	12.8	20.0	12.4	down
1911	1914	3	12.4	16.3	13.6	up
1914	1921	7	13.6	27.2	12.5	down
1921	1924	3	12.5	14.4	13.0	up
1924	1927	3	13.0	14.0	12.9	down
1927	1932	5	12.9	18.1	5.6	down
1932	1938	6	5.6	13.2	10.0	up
1938	1949	5	10.0	22.0	19.2	up
1949	1958	9	19.2	41.8	25.8	up
1958	1961	3	25.8	32.1	29.9	up

*Prices in cents per pound; war years are excluded.

The material in the last four tables deserves a comment or two, particularly with regard to recent interest in price control schemes (which, as a topic, will be taken up later). It is hoped that at this point the reader appreciates the difficulties with which members of a cartel must grapple when hard times descend—that is, when creditors, stockholders, boards of directors, or, when these facilities are the property of the state, voters and employees start asking the old question, "Just how did we get into this situation?" Of course, the compulsion to chisel, as it is called, is present even during the rosiest of times; but when things start going bad it becomes overwhelming. Most important, it is necessary to chisel *first,* that is *now,* because it usually works out that this type of problem takes a while to go away, and the longer one waits, the worse it becomes. It is, in fact, pressures of this nature that have, at least until the present day, made it impossible to sustain worldwide cartels of the classical type.

At the same time it should be accepted that the logic leading to corporate liaisons of some sort is very difficult to counter in the case of copper. Anyone familiar with this market realizes that through overinvestment and technological progress in the matter of substitutes, producers are always in danger of finding themselves faced with a chronically depressed market. The temptation to regulate the price is thus always near, at least for some producers; and this is particularly true now that the economic health of entire countries, as well as corporations, depends on what happens on the metal exchanges.

In examining the previous tables one could make a case for distinguishing about twelve price cycles since the turn of the century (excluding the World War II and the cycle in which we are at present). There are definite trends observable in each peak price to peak price cycle, with about half on a rising trend and the rest on a falling. A similar observation would result if we had gone from trough to trough, although here "up" trends tend to dominate.

Fluctuations are also quite easily detectable in these tables. For instance, in 1964 it can be seen that on the London market the percentage deviation between the highest and the average price was 50.5 percent. Deviations of this type are, of course, accountable to speculation—in this case, speculation accompanying the tag end of the valorization experiment. Two observations are prompted by this information. The first, concerning price cycles, makes it clear that if international commodity agreements are to come about, they should probably be valid for a period that would cover the average cycle length, and perhaps the length of the longest cycle (about eight years). And then, if some sort of international or semi-international organization is to be established to systematize price stabilization efforts, it must somehow devise rules that would permit it to cope with aberrant deviations on the order of 50 percent above or below the average price, without making these deviations worse.

Finally, it should be noted that the full employment-steady growth policies that we have seen a great deal of since the World War II have undoubtedly done a great deal to weaken fluctuations originating on the demand side of the market. If, in fact, we lump such phenomena as strikes in with divine intervention, it might be possible to argue the possibility of eliminating most fluctuations through controlling, either directly or indirectly, the effect of inventories on price formation. The indirect means of doing this, at least in theory, would be the establishment of a central inventory, or buffer stock, of such size and efficiency that all other inventories would be compelled to follow its lead in buying or selling. Whether this could be done in practice, however, remains to be seen.

THE ECONOMICS OF EXHAUSTIBLE RESOURCES

The intention of introducing the economics of exhaustible resources is to develop some rules similar to the "marginal relations" of elementary economic theory.[1] But before beginning this operation, it might be useful to point out that the obtaining of a mineral generally involves three stages: exploration, development, and extraction, and different types of costs can be associated with each stage.[2]

Exploration costs are difficult to pin down, since they affect other costs; and a direct imputation is extremely difficult, if not impossible. This should not be reason to think, however, that these costs are inconsiderable. The general situation in regard to geological information is to a surprising degree unsatisfactory in both developed and less developed countries, and where the latter are concerned, estimates must be taken with extreme caution.

In general, the mapping of mineral deposits requires many years. In Zambia, for instance, eight years were spent plotting the copper belt deposits. It is still true to some extent that in spite of advances in surveying techniques (which use aerial, geophysical, and geochemical methods), pre-production costs associated with a modern competitive mining venture often are prohibitive. This is particularly true in less developed countries, because while in developed economies the national geological surveys provide a base for mineral explorations, this facility is for the most part nonexistent elsewhere. It also appears that mineralogical surveys are not being started on a particularly large scale in underdeveloped regions.

Turning now to the problem of maximizing benefits relative to costs over time, an interesting background to this topic has been provided by Gordon [1967]. What he has done in particular is to emphasize the part that user cost theory has to play in the economics of production from natural resources, where in this type of analysis user cost theory studies the influence that market conditions in the future have on current output decisions, and thus includes the pure theory of exhaustion as a special case.

Essentially what we have here is a recognition that for the producer, a mineral in the ground is a stock which, if used today, is unavailable in the future. Profit maximization then means that revenue must cover not only marginal costs but also the present value of unit profits given up by producing during the present period instead of later: if we produce today instead of at some point in the future, the discounted value of future profits must be less than the profit

---

[1] The "discrete" portion of the algebraic analysis that follows is taken from my paper, "The Economics of Exhaustible Resources: A Note" [1971b].

[2] Just how these costs have been computed and allocated is taken up in some detail by Bradley [1967]. For the elementary economics of this type of market, the reader is referred to Appendix A of this book.

realizable through present production, since neglecting this latter factor involves an overly rapid rate of exploitation.

The first step in the algebraic analysis is to set out the elements that we are dealing with. The extraction of q_t in each period carries with it a unit cost c_t, and each q_t commands a unit price p_t. Gordon has taken p_t and c_t independent of q_t, but the assumption here will be $p_t = p_t(q_t)$ and $c_t = c_t(q_t)$. Also, considering that there are alternative uses of financial resources, it is the discounted values that are of interest to us. A discount factor r will thus be used, and for simplicity it will be taken as constant. With T as the time horizon, perfect foresight, and a discounted unit profit of

$$\pi_t = \frac{p_t - c_t}{(1 + r)^t}$$

for each period, the following nonlinear program can be written:

$$\text{Max: } Z = \frac{p_t q_t - c_t q_t}{(1+r)^t} = \pi_1(q_1)q_1 + \ldots\ldots + \pi_T(q_T)q_T = F(q_1,\ldots,q_T)$$

$$\text{With: } q_1 + q_2 + \ldots\ldots\ldots + q_T \leqslant \bar{K} \tag{1}$$

$$\text{And: } q_1, q_2, \ldots\ldots q_T \geqslant 0$$

The above is a typical nonlinear program, where Z is the objective function and $\bar{K}$ the total amount of the exhaustible resource available at the time of making the production (i.e., extraction) decision. It should be observed that it is possible for less than the available amount of the resource to be extracted. In fact, it is conceivable that if price is too low relative to cost and there are alternative uses of the resources used in extraction, there will be no extraction at all. It is now instructive to write the dual of equation (1). This is:

Min: $\qquad Z = \lambda \bar{K}$

$$\lambda \geqslant \frac{\partial F}{\partial q_1} = F'_1$$

$$\lambda \geqslant \frac{\partial F}{\partial q_2} = F'_2$$

Subject $\qquad \bullet$ $\qquad\qquad\qquad\qquad\qquad\qquad$ (2)
to: $\qquad\quad \bullet$
$\qquad\quad \bullet$
$\qquad\quad \bullet$

$$\lambda \geqslant \frac{\partial F}{\partial q_T} = F'_T$$

And: $\qquad \lambda \geqslant 0$

In this dual $\partial F/\partial q_i = F'_i$ represents the value of the discounted marginal profit for period "i." We thus see immediately that λ is the shadow price of the resource $\bar{K}$, or the opportunity cost of holding the resource unmined. If $\lambda = 0$ we have $\Sigma q_i < \bar{K}$, and some of the resource is left unmined at the end of the time horizon T. Similarly, when $\lambda > \partial F/\partial q_i$ there is no production during period "i," or $q_i = 0$. A diagramatical representation of this situation can be found in Figure 1–2. What this figure shows is planned production for periods $1, \ldots, T$ at the beginning of the first period. At the beginning of the second period another production plan, based on information available at that time, is made and so on.

As shown, planned production at the beginning of the first period calls for the exhaustion of $\bar{K}$ during the time horizon T, and thus we have $\Sigma q_i^* = \bar{K}$. Also notice that $q_2^* = 0$, which signifies that for the second period the opportunity cost, λ^*, of leaving the mineral for extraction in a later period exceeds any value of the discounted marginal profit during that period. The reader should consider, however, the consequences of a change, at the beginning of the first period, in the value of the predicted marginal profit for the second period due, for example, to a strong increase in the predicted value of p_2. This would result in the "F" curve for the second period shifting up and to the right, thus causing a rearrangement of planned intertemporal production, with q_2^* now perhaps greater than zero. If the expected p_2 increased without limit, we could

Figure 1–2. Diagrammatic Representation of a Solution to Equations (2).

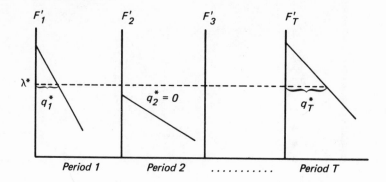

find ourselves with a situation where all production should be planned for the second period.

Some of this can be put more compactly by employing some results from optimal control theory.[3] In particular, if we wish to emphasize the non-negativity conditions on the q's, they could be introduced directly into the analysis. Thus we get:

$$L(q, \lambda, u, t) = \pi(q, t)e^{-rt} - \lambda(t)q(t) + u(t)q(t)$$

where we have:

$$q(t) = -\dot{K}, \; q(t) \geqslant 0$$
$$K(0) = \bar{K}, \; K(T) \geqslant 0$$
$$u(t) \geqslant 0$$

The optimal conditions then satisfy:

$$\frac{\partial L}{\partial q} = \left(\frac{\partial \pi}{\partial q}\right)e^{-rt} - \lambda + u = 0$$

$$\lambda(t) = \lambda^*, \text{ where } \lambda^* > 0, \; \lambda^* K(T) = 0$$

and:

$$u(t)q(t) = 0$$

From this we have that if $q(t) > 0$, then $u(t) = 0$, and $(\partial \pi / \partial q)e^{-rt} = \lambda^*$. Conversely, if $(\partial \pi / \partial q)e^{-rt} < \lambda^*$, then $u < \lambda^*$, from $q(t)u(t) = 0$.

[3]See, for example, Arrow [1967].

Chapter Two

The Structure of Ownership

The key to understanding the present structure of ownership in the copper industry involves no more than understanding the major importance of copper as an industrial input, the relatively large amount of investment required to obtain economical quantities of the material, and the sophisticated engineering and organizational techniques that are required in the procession from ore to final material. Thus, from about the turn of the century, it has been obvious to almost all serious students of the industry that there is room for only a few firms in this market; and that when new deposits were discovered it would be the established firms that have the expertise and financial support to take the best advantage of these discoveries. When, for example, geological reports describing huge deposits of copper in Africa and South America began making the rounds, no one was surprised to see these deposits secured, in one way or another, by the major copper producers and/or refiners of Europe and North America. As a result a situation developed where most of the capacity on these two continents was controlled either directly or indirectly from abroad, which meant that many of the decisions having to do with output, employment, and the development of capacity in these installations were also in external hands. As far as I have been able to find out, this was not an extremely popular arrangement with many individuals and political groups in the countries affected, and probably explains a large part of the bad feeling that eventually led to the nationalization of some of these properties.

Before going deeper into the matter of just who owns what, it might be interesting to add a little to the discussion of the previous chapter, as well as to borrow some information from future chapters. During the decade 1960–69 the average (unweighted) annual compound rate of growth of crude and refined copper (plus the direct use of copper scrap) was about 4 or 5 percent. This growth, however, varied widely among countries and regions, ranging from about 3 percent in the Western European Countries (E.E.C.) to about 12 percent for

Japan. In addition, these rates of growth have not been steady during this decade. There has been a steady increase for the socialist countries of Eastern Europe, while there have been ups and downs for the capitalist countries—depending upon the business cycle and prices. It even appears to be the case that the United Kingdom has been experiencing a negative rate of growth of consumption. Table 2–1 shows the consumption of refined copper plus scrap.

The matter of consumption per head deserves a closer look. If we examine the situation for certain developed and developing countries for the year 1968 we have results as shown in Table 2–2.

The next step after examining these tables is to emphasize the geographical concentration displayed in the consumption of copper. The United States was responsible for a quarter of the world's consumption of crude copper in 1969, and about a third of the world's consumption of refined copper plus scrap. Other major consumers were the E.E.C. with about one-fifth of world consumption of both crude and refined plus scrap, Japan with 12 percent of both categories, the U.S.S.R. with a recorded consumption of 14 percent crude, and the U.K. with about 7 percent of both groups.

All told, about four-fifths of world copper consumption takes place in the *major* market economy industrial countries. As for per capita consumptions, these are not without interest. Per capita consumption of copper in the U.K. was about 15.7 pounds in 1969—down from 19.6 in 1960. The U.S. consumed 16 pounds in 1969 as compared to 11.7 in 1960, and the E.E.C. figure

Table 2–1.   Consumption of Refined Copper plus Scrap

	Consumption* 1960	Consumption* 1969	Growth Rate 1960–69	Proportion of World Consumption 1960	Proportion of World Consumption 1969	Per Capita Consumption[†] 1960	Per Capita Consumption[†] 1969
Developing countries	225	345	4.9	3.6	3.8		
Developed countries (market economies)	5,095	7,476	4.4	81.8	81.3		
E.E.C.	1,408	1,919	3.5	22.6	20.9	8.2	10.25
United Kingdom	734	686	-0.8	11.8	7.5	14.02	12.35
United States	1,866	2,878	4.9	29.9	31.3	10.33	14.16
Japan	504	1,147	9.6	8.1	12.5	5.41	11.21
Socialist countries (Europe)	802	1,190	4.5	12.9	12.9		
U.S.S.R.	652	930	4.0	10.5	10.1	3.04	3.87
Other East Europe	150	260	6.3	2.4	2.8		
Total world	6,232	9,191	4.4			2.08	2.59

Source: World Metal Statistics and UNIDO Documents.

* Consumption in thousands of metric tons.

† Per capita consumption in kilograms.

Table 2–2. Per Capita Consumption* of Copper in All Forms

Selected Developed Countries		*Selected Developing Countries*	
Austria	4.5	Colombia	0.1
Belgium	6.8	Venezuela	0.6
France	7.5	Iran	0.2
W. Germany	11.7	Israel	2.9
United Kingdom	11.2	Phillipines	0.1
Italy	6.5	Thailand	0.1
Japan	9.6	Algeria	0.1
Netherlands	7.9	Ghana	0.1
Scandinavia	9.0	Libya	0.5
Switzerland	10.7	Morocco	0.2
United States	12.1	Tunisia	0.1
		Zambia	0.1

Source: UNIDO Document ID/WG 74/4.

* Per capita consumption in kilograms per head.

was 13.1 pounds in 1969 compared to 11.3 in 1960. Japan's consumption increased by a factor of almost three during this period—15 pounds against 5.8; while in the U.S.S.R. consumption increased from 5.60 to 7.33 pounds per capita. In the less developed world, consumption is quite low: only about 3.5 percent of the world's total refined consumption. A high per capita consumption is tantamount to a high level of industrialization; and while these countries will probably see their importance as producers increased in the coming years, the majority of them can hardly be expected to alter their relatively slow pace of development for some time yet.

As for the matter of production, Table 2–3 gives an oversight of world mine production in 1960 and 1969.

Table 2–3.   Mine Production of Copper by Main Producing Areas*

	1960	1969	Rate of Increase (%)
Developed areas			
U.S.A.	979.9	1,413.4	4.2
Canada	398.5	500.2	2.5
Socialist countries	625.2	1,083.0	6.3
Western Europe	127.4	202.5	5.3
South and S.W. Africa	69.7	152.6	9.1
Australia	111.2	128.1	1.6
Japan	89.2	120.3	3.4
Total developed	2,401.1	3,600.1	4.6
Less developed areas			
Zambia	576.4	719.5	2.5
Zaire (Congo)	302.3	369.8	2.1
Other Africa	33.0	39.5	2.0
Chile	532.1	686.8	2.9
Peru	181.7	199.0	1.0
Other South and Central America	82.0	94.3	1.6
Other Asia	126.0	204.9	5.6
Total less developed	1,833.5	2,308.8	2.6
World total	4,234.5	5,908.9	3.8

Source: Metal Statistics and Metallgesellschaft 1970.
*In thousands of metric tons.

A similar construction in Table 2–4 shows refined copper production in 1960 and 1969.

CONCENTRATION AND INTEGRATION IN THE COPPER INDUSTRY

In 1960, the U.S., Britain, and Belgium controlled about 84 percent of the world's known commercial copper deposits. (This figure has changed considerably due to various nationalizations of one degree or another.) In the U.S., five companies controlled 76 percent of total smelting capacity, and refining showed a similar tendency. Where the user side is concerned, the arrangement at the present time is that the production of semi-fabricates is largely answered for by about thirty-five companies, mostly wire and brass mills. Many of these fabricators are, in turn, affiliated with the major producers of copper products.

By 1970, eleven parent companies, one consortium, and three government corporations controlled 81 percent of the total world supply outside of the socialist countries of Eastern Europe and Asia. As far as I know, however, the U.S.S.R. is the only major producer of any importance among the socialist

Table 2–4.   Refined Copper Production*

	1960	*1969*	*Rate of Increase (%)*
Developed areas			
U.S.A.	1,642.6	2,026.5	2.4
Canada	378.2	408.8	1.0
Socialist countries	799.9	1,262.0	5.2
Western Europe	970.9	1,229.3	2.7
Japan	248.1	629.2	10.9
Australia	84.2	137.3	5.5
South Africa	11.8	61.2	20.1
Total developed	4,135.7	5,754.3	3.7
Less developed areas			
Zambia	402.6	598.1	4.1
Zaire (Congo)	144.7	183.3	2.7
Other Africa	1.2	20.7	37.2
Chile	225.6	453.0	8.0
Other Central and South America	60.6	108.4	6.7
Other Asia	23.4	29.7	2.7
Total less developed	858.1	1,393.2	5.5
World total	4,993.8	7,147.5	4.1

Source: Metal Statistics and Metallgesellschaft 1970.
*In thousands of metric tons.

countries, and its production is handled by a government corporation. Thus, for an output in excess of Zambia's we add another unit on the ownership side. In the same year ten American companies owned about 94 percent of the U.S. copper mining capacity.[1] As Table 2–5 illustrates, very similar statements could be made about the world's refining capacity.

In conjunction with Table 2–5, it might be of interest to point out that thirty-four companies and government corporations accounted for about 94 percent of world refining capacity in 1969. In addition, as should be evident by now, the subject of concentration is to a considerable degree interlocked with that of integration. Rough estimates exist which indicate that Anaconda, Phelps Dodge, Kennecott, and American Smelting and Mining together possess about 65 percent of U.S. fabricating capacity. In fact, as brought out in a lecture given

[1] I would like to emphasize that in this chapter I am merely stating facts about ownership; and I am not attempting to attach any ethical significance to the material presented here. As far as I am concerned, large units are a fact of life in the mining industry although, the reader should note, the world copper industry consists of thousands of smaller units. In Chile, for instance, there were 3,500 smaller mines in 1970.

Table 2–5.   Leading Suppliers of Refined Copper*

Country	Firm	Est. Market Supplies (%)
U.S.A.	Anaconda	11.6
Bermuda (U.K.)	Anglo American	8.3
U.S.A.	Kennecott	7.5
U.S.A.	American Metal Climax	7.3
U.S.A.	Ascaro	7.0
U.S.A.	Phelps Dodge	6.2
Canada	Noranda Mines	3.5
Canada	Newmont Mining	2.9
Belgium	Union Miniere	2.8
Canada	International Nickel	2.6
Germany	Norddeutsche Affinerie	2.3
Japan	Mitsuibishi	2.0
Japan	Nippon Mining	1.9

*Prior to major nationalizations; and government corporations excluded.

by Houthakker in 1970,[2] Kennecott, Phelps Dodge, Anaconda, and Ascaro have wholly or partly owned fabricating subsidiaries that are among the largest fabricating firms in the U.S.

As I described the copper industry in the previous chapter, a series of well-defined steps from mining through the production of end uses can be delineated, with each step belonging to a sort of stage in the industry. But where ownership is concerned, this pattern began to break down a good many years ago—first through lateral, and then vertical, integration. In North America integration existed right from the beginning, since the shape of the industry was largely dictated by the presence of large-scale domestic mining, as well as a growing market with many oligopolistic and oligopsonistic features, and an important influence being exerted right across the industry by a handful of financial institutions.

In Europe, and particularly in England, the first wave of integration came about through the combining of end users. Next it was the fabricators who felt that they were at the mercy of their customers, and were in fact caught between producers on one side and end users on the other. First these fabricators went together, and then in one way or another united with end users, the resultant combination regarding itself as manufacturers of copper products.

It should be made clear, however, that there are very strong—and perhaps legitimate—economic forces making for integration, and these are nowhere more evident than when one considers the end users of copper. When the end-use industry features very large producing units, and when the input is of considerable importance, integration tendencies are usually very pronounced. The argument here is that if there was a major price increase for the input, a large

[2] See also "Report of the Subcommittee on Copper to the Cabinet Committee on Economic Policy," The White House, Washington, D.C., 18 May, 1970.

Table 2–6. The Zambian Mining Industry: Some Basic Information

Company Mine	Anglo-American and Zambian Government			Roan Selection Trust and Zambian Government		
	Nchanga	Bancroft	Rhokana	Mufulira	Baluba	Luansha
Where smelted	Rhokana		Rhokana	Mufulira	Luansha	Luansha
Where refined	Rhokana		Rhokana	Mufulira		Luansha
Mining capacity*	240,000	65,000	97,000	174,000		105,000
Estimated total reserves (1968)				164,550,000	112,000,000	82,459,000
Ore grade				3.24	2.70	2.85
Estimated production cost, U.S. cents/lb (1968)†	28.0	30.0	32.5	24.4		28.3

Notes:

1. Total refining capacity (1969): Anglo-American 168,000 mt, Roan Selection 152,000 mt, Zambian govt. 333,000 mt.

2. Latest expansion plans (1972): Nchanga consolidated to expand by 1975–76 to 500,000 metric tons per year; Baluba mine to begin operation about 1973–74; Mufulira Refinery to be expanded to 75,000 metric tons per year of electrolytic copper.

3. Total amount owed foreign mining interests (1972): $232.96 million out of the original debt of $292.6 million.

* Metric tons per year.

† Excluding royalties and export taxes.

Table 2–7. The Chilean Mining Industry: Some Basic Information

Company (Mine)	Chuquicamata	El Salvador	El Teniente	Santiago Mining (ENAMI)*	Mantos Blancos	Exotica
Smelted	Chuquicamata	Potrerillos	Caletones			Probably Chuquicamata
Refined	Chuquicamata (Formerly) Raritan Copper Works, U.S.A.	Some Chile (Formerly) Raritan Copper	Caletones† (Fire Refined Las Ventamas (Elec. Ref.)	Las Ventamas		Probably Chuquicamata
Refining capacity (1969)	406,000 (Electrolytic)		50,000 (Electrolytic) 60,000 (Fire Ref.)	84,000 (Elec.)		
Sales	(Formerly) Anaconda Sales Co., N.Y. Some long-term contracts with Japan	(Formerly) Anaconda Sales Co., N.Y.	(Formerly) Kennecott Sales Some long-term contracts with Japan		Sudami (Brussels)	
Production (1969) metric tons	283,000	77,000	180,000	52,800	30,000	36,000
Ore grade (average yield) %	1.25	1.60	1.20		1.90	1.35

Notes:

1. Official Chilean estimate of total reserves (1969) are 59 million metric tons.

2. Total electrolytic refining capacity in 1969 given as 560,000 metric tons.

3. Capacity planned for the near future (1972) according to the Copper Industry Development Plan: Chuquicamata (354), El Salvador (100), Exotica (102), El Teniente (275), Rio Blanco (61), Mantos Blancos (31), Disputata Group (40.3), ENAMI (82.7), Others (61.4). These figures are in thousands of metric tons, and the *planned total output* is 1,107,000 metric tons.

4. Prices at which the majority of Chilean copper was sold up to 1970: LME, Engineering and Mining Journal European Average, Engineering and Mining Journal U.S. Average.

5. Other than the U.S., investment in mining in Chile came from Canada (Noranda and Javelin), France (Group Penarroya), and Japan (Dowa and Nippon Mining).

* ENAMI (Empresa Nacional de Mineria): The government agency for the support and promotion of the mining industry.

† A part of Teniente's smelted output shipping as blister.

cent of refining capacity (the Las Ventanas Refineries), and the nationalization laws of 1967 gave the Chilean government 51 percent of local assets. The intention at that time was to establish an agreement similar to that discussed for Zambia: management and sales would be handled by Anaconda and Kennecott in return for fees that were to be mutually agreed upon. (In the case of Anaconda this was to be 1 percent of gross sales, plus costs and expenses.) Strict control, however, was to be maintained over foreign activities in the mining sector, particularly by the government corporation CODELCO (Corporación del Cobre), which would review and approve all contracts for the sale of Chilean copper and audit the operations of foreign companies. Where the disposition of local mine output is concerned, data in Table 2–7 were relevant until quite recently.

It should once again be emphasized that the information in Table 2–7 no longer represents the situation in Chile. The present government, as of July 11, 1971, assumed responsibility for the assets of all the North American companies in the copper sector. Some negotiation has taken place to determine what compensation—if any—these firms are going to receive, but at the present time the North American organizations are also out of the management and sales picture.

The situation for Zaire (formerly the Congo) is somewhat more complicated. Until 1967 all copper production in the Congo was managed by one company, and the same was true for smelting and refining—which was done either in the Congo or in Belgium. This company was the Union Minière du Haut Katanga. After the nationalizations, its functions were taken over by Societe Generale Congolaise des Mines (Gecomines), a 100 percent government-owned company. In 1969 and 1970 the government chartered three other companies.

At present Gecomines is still the most important mining enterprise in the country. It produced 83 percent of Zaire's mineral exports in 1969, and this in turn gave 60 percent of the country's foreign exchange earnings. Sales for the company is handled by Societe Generale des Minerais de la Belgique (SMG), a Belgium firm, which also provides management and recruitment services. Zaire's output goes mostly to the E.E.C., Scandinavia, Japan, and India.

In 1969 the Société de Développement Industriel et Minere du Congo (Sodimico) came into being. It has been authorized two mining "concessions." Beginning in 1973, the entire output of this enterprise will be shipped to Japan for smelting and further processing. Two more companies were organized in 1970. These involve a foreign consortium and the government, and the companies are called Simico and Socotef. As in the previous case they have been granted concessions, and the latest information has it that their investment may amount to at least 300 million dollars. It might also be of some interest to present a recent estimate of future copper production in Zaire-Congo (see Table 2–8).

These figures in Table 2–8 could, of course, be changed at any time, with the probable direction being upward. The figures in Table 2–9 correspond to those presented earlier in this section.

Table 2–8.   Projected Output in Zaire: 1973–1980

Year	Gecomines	Sodimico	Simico/Socotef	Total
1973	485,000	45,000		530,000
1974	510,000	65,000		575,000
1975	530,000	140,000	110,000	780,000
1976	555,000	140,000	110,000	805,000
1977	580,000	140,000	110,000	830,000
1978	610,000	140,000	110,000	860,000
1979	635,000	140,000	110,000	885,000
1980	660,000	140,000	110,000	910,000

Source: American Embassy, Kinshasa.

At the present time there is very little, if any, further processing of copper in the country. However, given the apparent flexibility of the present government in the matter of foreign capital, such operations are not unthinkable. The key factor in determining the possibilities for further processing is probably, at the present time, the availability of trained manpower.

The copper industry in Peru is, for the most part, dominated by foreign parent companies, mostly American. Principal owners are Cerro Corporation, with 47.3 percent of Peru's mine output; American Smelting and Refining, 34.3 percent; Phelps Dodge, 9.6 percent; and Newmont Mining Corporation, 6.1 percent. This situation, however, has been somewhat modified by the mining decree of 16 April, 1970, in which a state mining company, Empresa Minera del Peru, will be in control of public activities in the mining sector, and will participate in new mining ventures by up to 25 percent. In addition, the government has expressed its intention to build a refinery every year with a capacity of 100,000 tons; and the sale of copper was to be more or less controlled by the state within eighteen months.

The mining law of June 1971 was designed to substantiate the above. In addition it contained provisions for a scheme of workers' participation in the equity capital of the mining companies by transfering shares to a "community" consisting of all the employees of a firm. The goal is to transfer 50 percent of equity to the community over an unspecified period of time.

Table 2-9.   The Zairein Mining Industry: Some Basic Information

Company	Gecomines*	Sodimico	Simico/Socotef†	SMG
Smelted	Lubumbashi	Domestic and abroad		
Smelter capacity	143,300 short tons			
Refined	Likasi-Shituru, Luilu, and Belgium	Japan		
Refinery capacity (short tons per year)	Lik-Shi: 203,900 st Luilu: 137,800 st			
Owned by:	Zaire Government	Govt. 15%‡ Japanese 85%	Govt. 20% U.S. 31% U.K. 28% French 7% Japanese 14%	Belgium Origin: Sales, Management Recruiting
Average ore grade (%)	Kamoto: 3.6 Musonoi: 5.2 Ruwe: 1.50 M'sesa: 4.10 Kakanda: 3.5–4.5 Kambove: 4.0 Kipushi: 4.4–5.6	Musoshi: 2.18 Kisenda: 5–6		
Notes:				

1. Sodimico to operate open pit mine and concentrator at Musoshi. Start up 1973–74, Capacity 53,000 tpy (tons per year).

2. Sodimico to mine 70,000–80,000 tpy at Kisenda. Start up date 1975–76.

3. Gecomines to expand capacity at Kamoto by 80,000 mtpy before 1975. Planned capacity: 460,000 (1975), 520,000 (1977), 600,000 (1980).

* Two companies: Societe Internationale des Mines du Congo, and Société Congolaise du Tenke-Fungurume.

† Generale Congolaise des Minerais.

‡ These companies are: Nippon Mining, Mitsui Mining and Smelting, Sumitomo Metal Mining, Farukawa Mining, Toho Zinc.

Table 2–10. Disposition of Peruvian Copper

Stage of Processing	Production	Exports	Export Destination
Ore	212,537	2,258	Japan
		758	Sweden
		222	Others
–Stocks	0		
–Exports	3,238		
Concentrates	209,269	16,884	Japan
		4,729	U.S.
		1,348	Sweden
		1,544	Others
–Stocks	0		
–Exports	24,505		
Blister	186,853	79,217	U.S.
		24,460	Belgium
		18,345	W. Germany
		16,956	Others
–Stocks	9,375		
–Exports	138,978		
Electrolytic Copper	38,500	24,154	U.S.
		3,110	Japan
		5,823	Others
–Stocks	2,109	5,823	
–Exports	33,807		
Semis	3,340	68	Denmark
		33	Others
	Residual . . . . 3230 = Domestic Use + Stocks + Unknown		

Source: Annuario Minero del Peru 1968, 1969, and World Bureau of Metal Statistics, and Brundenius, 1972.
Note: Units are metric tons.

Table 2–11 is similar to the tables presented earlier in this chapter. What it does not show, however, is the involvement of some of the copper mining organizations in the economy as a whole. There are, for instance, about 220 mining companies in Peru, and about 100 of these are controlled to one degree or another by Cerro de Pasco (the parent company related to Cerro Corporation of New York), which also appears to have interests in explosives, railroads, and so on. There would also seem to be an extensive representation, on the boards of directors of the larger firms, of the more prominent members of the local community.

In examining the disposition of Peruvian copper as given in Table 2–10, the reader is referred to Chapters 1 and 6 where descriptions of the mining final-use cycle are to be found.

Table 2–11.   The Peruvian Mining Industry: Some Basic Information

Company	Cerro de Pasco	Southern Peru	North Peru	Cerro Verde	Cuajone	Antamin	Tintayo
Smelted	Oraya	Ilo	?				
Refined	Oraya	Outside Projected Ilo					
Refinery capacity (tons/year)	35,000	150,000 (Projected)					
Production capacity (tons/year)	73,500	130,000	7,500	30,000			18,000
Start up				1974–75		1975–76	1975–76
Reserves (million tons)				250			
Owner	Cerro Corp.	Asarco Cerro Phelps-Dodge Newmont	Asarco	M.P.*	South. Peru	M.P.*	M.P.*
Ore grade (%)		Cuajone: 1.00 Quellaveco: 0.95		1.1	1.0		

Notes:

1. Cerro Verde, Cuajone, Antamin, and Tintayo are new projects. Other new projects are Michiquillay Mine, the ownership of which is to be 51 percent M.P. and 49 percent Japanese; and Ferro/Chalcobamba, 51 percent M.P. and 49 percent Granges (Sweden).

2. The Peruvian government has entered into talks with Cerro. Corp., the end results of which are intended to be the transfer of ownership of Cerro de Pasco to the Peruvian government.

*M.P. = Minero Peru, the government corporation.

Table 2–12. Principal Producers: U.S.

Company	Smelted and Refined	Sold By
Kennecott	Own plant; some to Asarco	Kennecott Sales
Phelps Dodge	Own plant	Phelps Dodge Sales
Anaconda	Own plant	Anaconda Sales Co.
Newmont Mining and Magma Copper	Own plant and Phelps Dodge	International Minerals and Mining
Asarco	Own plant	Asarco
Copper Range	Own plant	Copper Range
Calumet	Own plant	Calumet
Quincy Mining	Own plant	Quincy Mining
Bagdad Copper	Asarco	Asarco
Duval	Asarco	Asarco and Duval Sales
Cyprus Mines	Asarco	Ametalco
Pima Mining	Phelps Dodge	
Tennessee Corp.	Own plant	Tennessee Corp.

Source: Yearbook of the American Bureau of Metal Statistics.

As is consistent with its industrial capacity, almost all of the mine output of the United States is smelted and refined in North America, although of late a small amount is being sent to Japan for smelting. Almost all fabrication from this output takes place in North America.

The larger U.S. mining companies operate their own smelters and refineries. The exceptions here are the Duval Corporation, Baghdad Copper, and Cyprus Mines, whose output is smelted and refined by Asarco and Phelps Dodge on a "custom basis." It should be inserted here that custom facilities generally involve the mining company paying a fee for the smelting and refining, and then disposing of the processed copper themselves. (However, in principle, there is nothing to prevent the custom smelter and refiner from taking over complete ownership of the copper.) That activities of custom smelters are of considerable importance is indicated by the fact that in North America about 8 percent of refined copper is sold at a so-called custom smelters' price. As compared to the producers' price, it tends to be relatively unstable, following, to a certain extent, the movements of the LME price.

On the basis of the previous tables and discussions, the reader should not conclude that entry into copper mining on a small scale is precluded. In addition to the large firms shown in Table 2–12, the U.S. mining sector contains a shifting clientele of smaller firms whose composition is determined by the price of copper. It seems more or less clear, however, that these smaller firms will never have more than a marginal significance where pricing and production in this particular industry is concerned.

Approximately the same thing can be said for the structure of the copper industry in Canada as in the U.S. It should be noted, however, that there is a definite Japanese presence in the Canadian copper industry that will be interesting to observe, since among other things the extent to which the Japanese become involved in Canada may determine their requirements from and involvement in the other copper-producing countries.

The principal producers of copper are given in Table 2–13. As for the smaller producing countries, a large part of the output of the less developed countries goes, in the form of ores and concentrates, to Japan or West Germany, while the smaller developed countries (Sweden, Australia, South Africa, etc.) smelt, refine, and sell their own mine output. Of course, a large part of this output is used in local industries. Mexico and India belong to the category of less developed countries that can process and absorb their own mine output.

Table 2–13.   Principal Producers: Canada

Company	Smelted and Refined	Sold By
International Nickel	Own plant	Own sales, and Ameltalco
Noranda Mines	Own plant	Noranda sales
Campbell Chibougamau	Noranda (Canada)	Noranda sales
Lake Dufault Mines	Noranda	Noranda sales
Maltoyami Lake	Noranda	Noranda sales
Normetal Mines	Noranda	Noranda sales
Patino Mining	Noranda	Noranda sales
Quemont Mines	Noranda	Noranda sales
Atlantic Coast Copper	Gaspe Copper, Noranda	Noranda sales
Gaspe Copper Mines Ltd.	Gaspe, Noranda	Noranda sales
Gullbridge Mines	Gaspe, Noranda	Noranda sales
Sherrit-Gordon Mines	Hudson Bay (S & M), Noranda	Noranda sales
Hudson Bay Smelting and Mining	Noranda	Noranda sales
Ecstall Mining	Noranda	Noranda, own sales
Anaconda (Canada)	Asarco (U.S.A.)	Anaconda sales
Asarco	Asarco	Asarco
Falconbridge Nickle	Own plant, some in Norway	
Bethlehem Copper	Sumimoto, Japan	Sumimoto, Japan
McIntyre Mines	Sumimoto, Japan	Sumimoto, Japan
Rio Algom	Sumimoto, Japan	Sumimoto, Japan
Solbec Mines	Sumimoto, Japan	Sumimoto, Japan
Western Mines	Sumimoto, Japan	Sumimoto, Japan
Craigmont Mines	Sumimoto, Japan	Sumimoto, Japan
Copperfields Mining Corp.	Sumimoto, Japan	Sumimoto, Japan

Source: Yearbook of the American Bureau of Metal Statistics.

Chapter Three

Copper Exchanges and Hedging, and the Trade in Copper

The two markets on which copper is quoted are the London Metal Exchange (LME) and the Commodity Exchange, Inc. (COMEX), which is located in New York. The LME is generally considered to be the most important of the two in terms of turnover, physical deliveries, and its influence on the pricing of copper in general: most of the "formulas" for pricing copper that are found on long-term contracts are related, in one way or another, to LME prices. However, COMEX handles a wider variety of metals, and it also provides facilities for trading hides and rubber.

The LME dates from 1882, although copper and other metals had been quoted in London much earlier. During World War II and the immediate post-war period, when the government controlled the price of strategic metals, the exchange was closed; but it reopened in 1953, and since that time a steady increase in activity has been noted. In 1968, with the world consumption of refined copper close to 7 million tons, approximately 2 million tons of copper 'futures' were traded on the LME. The amount of sales resulting in physical deliveries was much smaller, ranging down to 12,000 tons per month. In fact, not since the early days of copper trading have physical deliveries via the LME amounted to much, since it would be prohibitively expensive for African or South American producers to deliver copper to LME warehouses when the final customer was in China or Japan. (There are eight LME warehouses and delivery places in the U.K., plus warehouses in Rotterdam, Hamburg, and Antwerp.) On the basis of the small amount of physical deliveries taking place on the LME, a number of arguments have been advanced that the exchange provides an unsatisfactory basis for pricing such a large proportion of the world's production.

These arguments will not be examined here, since those with which I am familiar lack either a scientific or a rational basis; however, it should be obvious that the importance of the LME (and COMEX) extends far beyond its rather limited capacity to handle physical copper. If, for instance, one shape of copper is at a premium over another, even small deliveries to the LME often result in reestablishing an equilibrium. As for the categories of buyers and sellers on the exchange, buyers are usually merchants acting on the part of customers desiring to make marginal adjustments in their stocks. Sellers are usually large producers selling small quantities, small producers selling excess production, and fabricators selling excess stock.[1]

The principal function of the LME, however, is to provide facilities for "hedging," or insuring against unfavorable price movements. This operation will be explained in detail shortly, but it should be noted that given the extreme volatility of the market—a volatility that is intensified by the floating exchange rates now becoming common—hedging must be considered essential. In addition, prices on the LME generally serve to establish, by one formula or another, the price at which copper changes hands in other transactions. For example, copper from the Bougainville installation mentioned earlier will be priced according to quotations on the LME during the period in which the copper is scheduled to be delivered. This arrangement is in general regarded as satisfactory by all parties, since the LME prices reflect changes in the demand-and-supply situation over the entire world, and generally without delay.[2]

By way of further examination of this problem, it might be interesting to examine the role of copper merchants and the part they play vis-à-vis the principle producers and consumers. First of all, it should be understood that an approximate balance on the market is achieved in bilateral deals between the major consumers and producers. Through the interaction of these actors we get a kind of basic price which, if the market were perfect (in regard to information, certainty, etc.) would not necessitate the presence of third parties, at least not in appreciable numbers.

As we know, however, the market is not perfect. Wars begin and end; there are strikes, elections, revolutions, and the like; and as a result the demand for copper moves up and down in a way quite unforseeable when contracts were drawn up—sometimes many months or years earlier. It is here that merchants make their entrance. Generally merchants buy and sell copper outside the principal producer-consumer channels. For the most part they do not invest in production facilities, but they can and will hold or finance stocks.

Merchants tend to make extensive use of independent refineries. They also buy a great deal of scrap for refineries handling secondary materials. Many of the physical deliveries on the LME result from the transactions of merchants; and by the same token they carry out arbitrage operations on a worldwide basis. They are usually busiest when the demand for copper is highest, since

[1] See Labys, Rees, and Elliott [1971].

[2] Among the criticism leveled at the LME is the claim that it reacts *too* fast, thus possibly helping to destabilize the market. However, it should be remembered that from 1945—53, when the LME was closed, the market still showed a pronounced instability. For some theoretical remarks on price movements, the reader is referred to Appendix A of this book.

during these periods more copper than ever will come from the smallest mines (i.e., mines that under normal circumstances are only marginal producers and possibly have not committed their production to any given refinery) or from scrap. These are also the periods when buyers or sellers are most likely to misjudge requirements and thus need the service of merchants.

In the United States, where there is more integration in the copper industry, merchants may be experiencing somewhat less scope for their energies than in Europe. For one thing, COMEX has a smaller physical turnover than the LME, and it is not especially oriented toward the international market. At the same time, however, its facilities for hedging and speculating are quite as developed as those to be found in London; and given the amount of communication between the two exchanges, COMEX can scarcely be accorded a lower category of importance.

The price at which most *merchant* copper is traded in the U.S. is related to the COMEX price. This price in turn, however, is not the same thing as the U.S. producer price, which generally has been lower than the LME price.[3] A great deal of the arbitrage that could take place between these two markets does not take place since, when demand is high, producers ration their sales. Some stock reductions, and a closing of the price gap, come about due to the ability of merchants to sell in European markets; but for the most part American producers frown on these operations, and it is believed that they have taken steps to see that their regular customers do not succeed in transferring any large amount of their excess copper to merchants and thus to the "free" market. On this point it is interesting to note that some producers, before 1961, reserved a portion of their output for sale to merchants. These transactions were later largely terminated (mostly at the insistence of the copper companies operating in Africa) on the grounds that sales of this type contributed to destabilizing the market, and many producers inserted "no resale" clauses in their contracts. It is probably true that similar no resale clauses are still employed by many American producers.

CONTRACT FORMS

On the basis of the latest regulations, three standard contract forms are available on the LME. These cover:

1. Electrolytic or fire-refined high conductivity wirebars, in standard sizes and weights.
2. Electrolytic copper cathodes, with a copper content not less than 99.90 percent; or first quality fire-refined ingot bars, with a copper content not below 99.7 percent.
3. Fire-refined ingot bars with a copper content not below 99.7 percent.

[3]The pricing of copper in the U.S. is taken up in Chapter 6.

Anyone can buy or sell on the LME, and the only limitation is that the sale must involve at least twenty-five long tons. The brand and place of delivery are chosen by the buyer; however, it should be remembered that by place of delivery we mean one of the LME warehouses. It is this provision that makes the LME of only limited interest to fabricators as a physical market, although many fabricators use the LME for hedging purposes.

COMEX operates with only one standard contract form. The basic commodity is electrolytic copper in wirebars, cakes, slabs, billets, ingots, and ingot bars, of standard weights and sizes, with a copper content of not less than 99.90 percent. (Silver is counted as copper.) Besides electrolytic copper, a number of other varieties of copper may be delivered at the *option of the seller.* (These include fire-refined high conductivity copper, lake copper, electrolytic copper cathods, etc.) Copper may be delivered from any warehouse in the U.S. that is licensed or designated by COMEX; but other warehouses must not be employed.

On the LME the three types of refined copper traded each have their own daily official quotations for both "cash" and "forward" deals. The cash quotation is called a settlement price, while the forward quotation is a three months' price. Three months is the maximum forward trading period on the LME, but trading can be for shorter periods. COMEX also provides cash and for-ward prices, and the period of forward trading must be within fourteen months, with delivery months limited to January, March, May, July, September, October, and December.

The presence of two prices, a cash and a forward price, has given rise to some interesting situations. Normally one would expect the forward price to exceed the spot price, an arrangement called a *contango;* but at various times the opposite situation has prevailed, and for extended periods. (The exceeding of the forward price by the spot price is called *backwardation.*) Since the LME forward price was customarily the one used for pricing by non-North American producers after they stopped using the price setting procedure known as *producer pricing,* the rather peculiar arrangement was often observed where fabricators bought at the forward price and sold on the LME at the spot. During the first part of the war in Vietnam, when backwardation was more the rule than not (sometimes by as much as 10 cents per pound) frequent dissatisfaction was expressed by many producers with the prevailing pricing arrangements, and at one time the Chilean government proposed employing the cash, rather than the forward price, as the basis for pricing. The Zambian government rejected this suggestion, claiming that it would have forced the price of copper up to still higher levels.

The economics of this last argument may appear rather confusing at first glance, since the conventional point of view is that an increase in the amount of copper offered on the spot market would have driven the spot price down, narrowing or perhaps even eliminating the backwardation. However, the fact remains that had copper been priced using the spot quotation, the cost of copper would have been increased by the amount of the backwardation, which in the short run would have meant as much as 25 percent. Under these circumstances, many consumers would have made strenuous efforts to find substitutes for copper. Since the Zambians knew this and were also aware that the widespread substitution of other materials for copper would be an economic disaster for Zambia, it becomes easier to understand their objections to the Chilean proposal.

HEDGING

This section will give an introduction to the topic of hedging. To simplify matters I will not employ a constant length of hedge in the examples given below, although the discussion is valid for *any* assumptions concerning hedge length. This point deserves mention, in fact, only because on the LME futures (or forward) contracts are for three months, while on COMEX they can be for any number of months up to fourteen, as long as delivery is scheduled for one of the delivery months specified by the exchange.[4] Thus, if the reader should detect some discrepancy between the operations being described here and those taking place on the LME, it is because I am in fact thinking in terms of COMEX. The principles being described, it should be remembered, apply equally to both exchanges.

   The first thing to examine is the futures contract. This contract specifies that a certain amount of copper—namely one unit, with one unit = 25,000 pounds—is to be delivered to one of the official delivery points, at such and such a price (where the supply and demand for these contracts determine the price). If the deal is for 250,000 pounds, then ten contracts are involved. The price entered on the contract is the price quoted on that day *for* the particular future date for which the deal is being made. For example, let us say that I buy a *May* futures some time in *January.* (The transaction, of course, is handled by my broker.) This means that in May I will be the proud owner of 25,000 pounds of copper, delivered into some warehouse hundreds, or even thousands, of miles from the University of Uppsala—if, that is, I do not *sell* a contract offsetting this purchase.

   But if, say in March, I tell my broker to sell a futures contract for 25,000 pounds, and assuming that he follows my instructions, I have erased the earlier purchase. In the books of my broker, we see the following:

Month		*Amount*	*Price*
January	Bought May Futures	25,000 pounds	x/pound
March	Sold May Futures	25,000 pounds	y/pound

[4]This is a small point, it turns out, since only a tiny percentage of all transactions culminate in deliveries. This point will be taken up shortly.

Assuming that $y > x + c$, where c is my broker's commission, I have made a profit, where the profit is $y - x - c$ (monetary) units per pound. (For example, if the monetary unit were cents, then the price and the profit would be in cents per pound. The *total* profit, in this example, would be 25,000 $[y - x - c]$ cents.)

Now, regardless of the actual service that may have been provided the market, or even mankind in general, by the above transaction, it seems clear on the basis of the given information that this particular transaction had its origin in the urge to gamble—that is, to take a chance that the price of futures would rise.

The question now becomes: why did I judge that the price of a futures contract would rise? The answer to that must be found in my judgment concerning the concrete supply-demand situation for copper in the future (in particular, during the period that I plan to hold my contract) and the fact that this situation should be reflected in the *spot* price of copper—that is, the *cash* price, or price of *present* copper. If I am extremely sophisticated, I might wish to modify my judgment based on simple supply and demand by considering the expected contango between present and future copper—that is, the price of future copper should normally be higher than that of present copper because of carrying charges, uncertainty, etc.

In the example just given for my purchase of a futures contract to make sense, it means that I expected—for one reason or another—the price of copper to rise, and as a result I would be able to sell my futures contract for a higher price than I bought it. On a day when the spot price of copper was x'. I bought a futures contract for x, with $x > x'$. Assuming that I made a profit, what happened was that at a later date, with the spot price at y', and the price of a relevant futures at y, with $y > y'$, I sold for y and made $y - x - c$, where c is a broker's commission. (Remember that the prices referred to here are the per pound price of copper.) Also, it should be observed that no assumption is being made that $x' - x = y' - y$. That is, the contango may change between the date of purchase and the selling date.

Naturally, if I expected the price to fall, I would sell a futures contract. Later I would buy a futures, thereby offsetting the earlier sale. As the reader can easily verify, if I sell a contract at w, and later buy at z, and $w > z$, then my per pound profit is $w - z - c$.

We have now accounted for one aspect of the futures market, that provided by speculators. (In the example given the speculator was, by implication, an amateur; but it happens that there are many professionals.) Another side is provided by what some people refer to as "legitimate" elements—individuals or firms who wish to insure against unfavorable price movements, either up or down. These are called hedgers. Some categories of hedgers will be given below, but first the reader should absorb the following rule:

> Those wishing to insure against a fall in price sell futures; while those wishing to insure against a rise in price buy futures.

Those wishing to insure against a fall in price are of course those who will sell in the future, at an unknown price; while those wishing to guard against a rise are those buying at an unknown price. As an example of a seller of futures we can take the following:

1. A miner sells copper for delivery three months in the future, at the price prevailing on the exchange on the day of delivery. Let us take 30 as the spot (cash) price of copper, and 32 as the price of a five-month future. The miner then sells a future for 32. Three months later he delivers his copper, with the spot price on the exchange on that day being 25, and the price of a two-month future (five months minus three months) at 26. He thus gets 25 for his copper and buys a future for 26, thus offsetting his earlier sale. His books read as follows:

> +32   sale of future
> +25   sale of copper
> −26   *purchase of future (offsetting)*
> +31   realized on sale of copper

The broker's commission should, of course, be subtracted from this to give the net value of the sale.

Using the same type of situation, let us take 30 as both the spot *and* the future price of copper when he signs his contract to deliver copper three months in the future. (Here we have no contango or backwardation on the date of signing the contract.) Then let 25 be the spot and 26 the futures price (for a two-month future) at the time he delivers his copper. His books in this case would read:

> +30   sale of future
> +25   sale of copper
> −26   *purchase of future (offsetting)*
> +29   realized on sale of copper

And this final figure is once again gross of the broker's commission. The thing to notice now is what would have happened had he not sold and bought a future, that is, hedged. His copper would have sold for 25 in both cases, and thus he would have lost 5 from the point of view of the spot price at the time of sale. By hedging he has "gained" 1 in the first case, while losing 1 in the second. (Both gain and loss are reckoned in regard to the initial spot price of 30 and are gross of the broker's commission.)

The question should also be asked: is there any chance that with a hedge he would lose in respect to the spot price prevailing on the date of delivery? Obviously, figures can be put in the above that would give this effect. Again, take 25 as the price of the copper at the time of delivery, and 34 as the price of a future pound of copper on the same date. We would then have for the value realized on the sale of the copper (if the conditions on the day of signing the contract were as in the first example given) $32 + 25 - 34 = 23$. In this case it would have been better not to hedge. At this point, however, it might be interesting to observe the contango. If we had a spot price of 30 on the day of signing the contract, we had on the same day a contango of 2. On the day of delivery the contango is 9. This change is regarded as abnormal. Normally the contango on the two dates would be much closer, in which case situations of this type would not occur.

Equally important, if abnormalities occur from time to time, they can go in either direction. For the hedger who is hedging on a regular basis, the law of averages should work to give him neither profit or loss. If he is dissatisfied with this arrangement, then he should join the speculators.

2. In the foregoing example the miner sold futures because he thought the price of copper would fall. By the same token, the buyer might be afraid that the price would rise, and so he would buy futures.Taking the figures in the first example given (where the spot price on the day the copper is bought is 30, and the futures price is 32) the buyer buys a contract for 32. If the spot price does rise to, for example, 40 cents per pound on the date of delivery, with futures price on that day at 41, the buyer sells his futures contract for 41 and pays 40 for the copper. His book now looks as follows:

    −32   purchase of futures
    +41   sale of futures (offsetting)
    −40   *purchase of copper*
    −31   paid for copper (gross of brokerage)

Notice what would have happened had the buyer not bought and sold a futures. He would have paid 40 for the copper. One of the things that should be emphasized here is that the hedger does not need to concern himself with the price movement. Hedging is insurance of a sort, and while he may gain or lose a small amount on each transaction, the idea is that in the long run his profits and losses should come close to balancing. This point can be further stressed by asking what would have happened had the price of spot copper fallen as it did in example #1 to 25, with the price of futures at 26 on the day of delivery. The books of the buyer would now be:

    −32   purchase of futures
    +26   sale of futures (offsetting)
    −25   *purchase of copper*
    −31   paid for copper (gross of brokerage)

One might now ask what would have happened had the buyer *forgot* the rule and began by selling instead of buying futures. In this case his book would take on the following appearance if the price rise situation is used:

+32   sale of futures
−41   purchase of futures (offsetting)
−40   purchase of copper
−49   paid for copper

To this is added the broker's commission—which, per pound, would of course be very small. (The broker's commission is normally levied on a contract. The profits and losses being considered in these examples are, as mentioned earlier, per pound and not per contract.)

One other example will be given here. This time a fabricator, in May, buys copper in the spot market for his inventory; at the same time he sells October futures contracts against it. In August he disposes of the finished product manufactured from the copper and then makes his offsetting purchase in the futures market. His bookkeeping is as follows:

May:	*Bought* spot copper at 30 cents/pound	*Sold* copper futures at 31.50 cents/pound
August:	*Sold* fabricated products containing copper on the basis of the prevaioing copper price of 27.50 cents/pound	*Bought* copper futures at 28.25 cents/pound

The *loss* on physical copper was 2.50, while the *gain* on futures was 3.25. Before paying his brokerage fee he has a gain of 0.75. Had no hedging taken place, the result would simply have been a loss.

Examples have been given here of hedges by miners, buyers, and fabricators; but, naturally, there are other possibilities. In fact anyone standing to lose should the price rise or fall probably should hedge. This includes ingot makers, smelterers, inventory holders, etc. Moreover, they will always be able to transfer their price risks as long as there is sufficient speculation in the market, and up to now this has always been the case.

THE TRADE IN COPPER

Due to the low metal content of most copper ores, there is comparatively little trade in "virgin" copper. Instead copper ores are usually first processed in installations located near the mine. This processing consists of crushing, grinding, and concentrating, with the entire sequence sometimes called milling. The concentrating usually manages to get the ore up to about 30 percent copper, and in this form a certain amount of trading is justified. In 1969 about 11 percent of world trade (by volume and in copper content) in nonfabricated primary copper was in concentrates. The principal exporters were Canada, Chile, Peru, and the

Phillipines, while the main importers were Japan, Germany, and the U.S. The U.S. imports generally from subsidiary companies, while much of the Japanese and German imports originated in firms whose financing was dependent, to some extent, on the importers.

The amount of blister copper traded came to about 29 percent of the total volume of nonfabricated copper. Refined copper, on the other hand, amounted to about 59 percent of the same category of world trade. The trade in semi-fabricates is a separate order of phenomenon and will be discussed later. Some information on this situation is given in Table 3–1.

Where the international movement of copper is concerned, "sales" from subsidiaries to parent companies at one time accounted for a sizable portion of trade. With the wave of nationalizations that began toward the middle of the 1960s, this type of trade decreased considerably. A similar category of trade is that taking place between the main producing companies and the large independent or semi-independent fabricators. These relationships were mostly conducted on the basis of annual contracts.

The evolving pattern of trade is built around long-term contracts. These contracts increasingly have as their basis financing arrangements in which "super" industrial powers such as Japan and Germany, themselves without mines but with sizable refining capacity, insure themselves of supplies over a five- to twenty-year future in return for building out the production facilities of the supplier company, or even becoming deeply involved in the general economic development of the country in which the supplier is located.

Japan, for example, has signed long-term contracts with firms in Canada, Australia, Indonesia, Bougainville, Malaysia, Chile, Zaire, Phillipines, etc., with many of these contracts running up to twenty years. Germany has also been active in many of these same countries and has, in addition, made long-term arrangements in Botswana. It seems to be the case, in fact, that given the large amounts that many of these financing deals involve, as well as the nature of these transactions—involving, as some of them do, the ownership but not the control of mining assets—that the aggregate trade in copper is tending to resemble the subsidiary-parent relationships so prevelant a few years ago.

As mentioned earlier, long-run contracts are for periods up to twenty years. For the most part they stipulate that the buyer will take so-and-so much per year, with a certain amount of discretion provided. The contract that the Japanese have with Bougainville Copper Property Ltd. calls for 1,000 thousand tons (copper content) of copper concentrate over the first fifteen years, with this being distributed as follows: 90,000 tons each of the first five years; 80,000 for each of the next five (with an option to purchase an extra 15,000 per year); and 30,000 tons per year for the last five years. The price is most often determined on the basis of prices on the LME, or a similar price. Thus the price at which the Japanese will get copper from Indonesia will be based on the average European

Table 3–1. 1969: World Trade in Copper Ores, Concentrate, and Refined

	Exports of			Gross Exports	Gross Imports
	Ores Concentrate, etc.	Blister	Refined		
Developing countries: total	255	634	1,260	2,149	84
CIPEC: total	101	612	1,260	1,974	
Chile	40	188	428	657	
Zaire	0	182	183	365	
Peru	30	134	34	198	
Zambia	31	108	615	754	
Other developing: total	154	23	0	175	84†
Phillipines	131	0	0	131	
Uganda	0	17	0	17	
Developed countries: total	180	133	989	1,302	not available
Australia	10	9	33	52	
Canada	143	0	191	334*	17*
South and S.W. Africa	0	95	26	121	3
Western Europe: total	26	25	529	580	2,250
Yugoslavia	0	0	18	18	32
Turkey	13	7	0	20	
U.S.A.	1	4	195	200*	370*
Japan			15	15	613

Source: Takeuchi 1972.

Note: Units are in thousands of metric tons.

*Includes trade in scrap.

† Brazil and India are significant net importers of copper.

selling price of copper originating in Zambia and Chile. These prices, in turn, will more likely than not be strongly correlated with LME prices.

In the general discussion of long-run contracts, the intergovernmental arrangements that the U.S.S.R. has with the other countries of Eastern Europe should perhaps be mentioned in passing. The U.S.S.R. supplies about 70 percent of primary copper imports in this part of Europe under arrangements often resembling those just discussed; and volume-wise the tonnage can be expected to increase in line with the general increase in production. Some figures on the exports and imports of the U.S.S.R. are given in Table 3–2.

As indicated in Table 3–2, a great deal of the trade in copper is still along traditional lines. A great deal of copper from Zaire (Congo) continues to move toward Belgium, while a large part of Zambian copper still finds its way to fabricators in the U.K. via networks established many years ago.

The traditional pattern, however, would now appear to be receding somewhat. One of the big reasons for this, of course, is the appearance of Japan as a major industrial power. As Figure 3–1 indicates, Japan stands with the E.E.C. as one of the two main hubs of international trading activity. The U.S. occupies a somewhat more modest role, although due to its becoming a larger importer of raw materials, this situation could conceivably change; but the links between the U.S. and its South American suppliers have weakened considerably of late, and just what this will lead to insofar as the future origin of U.S. imports is concerned cannot be predicted at the present time. However, I think it safe to say that just now many producers do not feel ill at ease in having to transfer a part of their sales from the U.S. to Japan, since Japanese buyers have made it quite clear that they expect the dynamic expansion that has been taking place in that country to continue for a good many years into the future.

Figure 3–1 shows the main trading flows for 1969. The Socialist countries are not shown, but, as already noted, a considerable part of the trade

Table 3–2. Imports and Exports of U.S.S.R.

Year	Mine Production (Copper Content)	Imports	Exports
1960	500	106	64
1961	550	82	60
1962	600	106	71
1963	600	88	72
1964	700	10	90
1965	750	1	93
1966	800	7	120
1967	825	1	94
1968	850	9	109
1969	875		

Source: World Bureau of Metal Statistics, *World Metal Statistics*, and Metallgesellschaft.
Note: Units in thousands of metric tons.

of Eastern Europe is internal. As for China, its copper requirements are increasing quite rapidly, and at the present time it gets most of its imports from the E.E.C. (in the form of refined and further processed) and from Zambia.

Figure 3–1. Approximate Principal Copper Trading Flows in Non-fabricates (000's of tons) Nonsocialist Countries (1969)

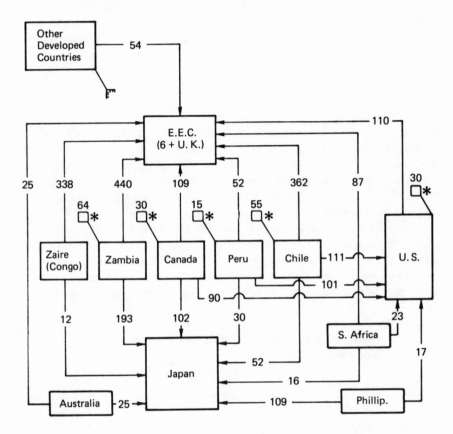

Note: Flows from Canada, Chile, and U.S. slightly underestimated because of (a) incomplete coverage of scrap, (b) exclusion of exports to such significant consumers as Argentina, Brazil, and India, (c) incomplete coverage of centrally planned economies.

◻* Indicates to "Other Developed Countries."

The flows shown in Figure 3–1 are of nonfabricated products. This still leaves room for a great deal of reexporting in copper products, since some countries import concentrates or blister, and export refined copper. In fact, it is not impossible to conceive of a pattern where ore and concentrates are imported and blister is exported, and subsequently refined is imported. Refining and smelting capacity is obviously a key factor in determining the origin and direction of a sizable percentage of these flows, particularly since (in 1966) the less developed countries refined only 55 percent of their own mine production, while smelting almost 90 percent. In 1966 the refining capacity in the main consuming countries was as given in Table 3–3. While there has been an increase in total refined consumption (and production), it is probably the case that the degree of self-sufficiency in refining capacity has not changed a great deal.

TRADE BARRIERS

This section makes a few comments on trade barriers, in particular tariffs, which means that attention will be paid to the international trade in semi-fabricates. The reason for this is that at the present time, none of the main importing countries have import duties on ores, concentrates, or—with the exception of Japan and the U.K.—unwrought copper, while semi-fabricates are subject to import duties in most of these countries.

The E.E.C. common external tariff places a duty of 10 percent on most semi-fabricates. In Japan most wrought copper products carry a duty of 20 percent, with a duty of 10 to 25 percent on most other items. The U.S. tariff includes a large number of sub-items relating to copper products, and most of these carry both a specific and an *ad valorem* duty. The total *ad valorem* equiva-

Table 3–3. Refined Consumption and Production: Major Consumers (1966)

Country	Total Refined Consumption	Total Refined Production
Germany	477	375
Belgium/Luxemborg	117	293
France	291	43
Italy	195	17
Netherlands	27	
U.K.	593	189
Scandinavia	133	97
Spain	66	63
Japan	486	405
U.S.A.	2,120	1,998

Source: Metallgesellschaft.
Note: Units are in thousands of metric tons.

lent is about 25 percent. (The specific tariff is 1.275 cents per pound, and the *ad valorem* duty is 22½ percent.)

Tariff reductions have been negotiated under the Kennedy Round, and in some cases these are considerable. In the U.S. most duties are to be cut by about one half. In the E.E.C. duties on the principal semi-fabricates will be reduced from 10 to 8 percent, while in Japan duties will be cut to 15 percent. Japanese duties on blister and refined copper are also to be reduced by about 10 percent. Table 3–4 summarizes post-Kennedy Round tariffs on copper products.

In connection with tariffs, it is proabably of interest to/comment on the often-voiced suggestion that the less developed among the producing countries should work toward an expanded export of semi-fabricates. Considering the difficulties that must be faced in any event should the production of semis be increased, even the post-Kennedy Round tariffs may be too high, and a comprehensive system of preferences would have to be introduced if these less developed producers are to become competitive in this market.

Among the reasons for this is the fact that freight charges per unit of value are generally higher for semi-fabricates than for metal, just as they are lower for metal than for ores. Similarly, crude metals are standardized products that can be sold in any market, while a certain percentage of semis are "custom" made, and close contact between manufacturer and end user is of considerable importance. Still, it seems to me that an overwhelming argument exists for the expansion, in some form, of this kind of activity. The lowering or abolishing of tariffs, establishing of preferences, or even subsidization of manufacturing installations should be looked upon as a substitute for certain types of development aid.

In conjunction with the material presented in Table 3–4, I have compiled table 3–5, showing some aspects of the trade in semi-fabricates.

Table 3–4.   Summary of Tariffs on Copper Metal and Semi
Manufactures (in Percents)

Country	Duty (%) Copper Metal	'Semis'	Tariffs
E.E.C.	0	8	
Japan	8.5	15	
U.S.*	3^a	$2-4^b$	a–B substantial part of imports would be suspen-ded from duties
			b–Rods, bars, plates, sheets, relatively unprocessed and seamless pipes and tubes. These items, together with copper wires, account for 90 percent of U.S. imports of semis.
		7^d	d–Wire, other than nickel silver
		$8-13^e$	e–Other items excluding nickel silver products
Denmark	0	0^a	a–Rolled and extruded products, of which the greatest cross-sectional dimension does not exceed 20 mm coiled
		$4-5^b$	b–Other semi-manufactures
Finland	0	$2-3^a$	a–Bars, rods, sections, and wire
		$4.5-5^b$	b–Plates, sheets, strip, tubes, and pipes
Norway	0	$0-0.3^a$	a–Semi manufactures other than tubes and pipes
		5^b	b–Tubes and pipes
Sweden	0	3^a	a–All semi manufactures
Switzerland	0.1	$1-4^b$	b–Some sub-items are subject to a duty of 5–6 percent
Austria	0	8^a	a–Unworked bars, rods, sections, plates, sheets and strip. Wire of 0.25 mm or more
		$9-10^b$	b–Worked bars, rods, sections, plates, sheet, and strip
		12^d	d–Unworked tubes and pipes and blanks therefor
		15^e	e–Worked tubes and pipes
Canada*	0^a	5^b	a–Unalloyed copper
			b–Bars, rods, plates, sheets, tubes
	5^d	10^e	d–Brass
			e–Electric wire

Source: Constructed from GATT Document COM. TD/71, 19 February, 1970
(Import Duties on Copper and Copper Products).
* The U.S. and Canadian tariffs are F.O.B. duties.

Table 3–5. Production and Trade in Semi-Fabricates

	Production		Imports	Exports
	Copper Semis	*Alloy Semis*	*Imports*	*Exports*
E.E.C.	1,042	724	33	136
Japan	700	339	2	43
U.K.	408	305	11	71
U.S.	1,671	889	153	13
Canada	228 (Total)		8	49

Source: Compiled from GATT Document COM. TD/71 19 February, 1970.
Note: All figures in thousands of short tons for copper and alloy semis.

Semi-fabricates are quite a different order of phenomenon from the other stages of copper. There are a number of different forms, sizes, and qualities of products, as well as different raw materials; and this makes a general discussion considerably more difficult than that which has concerned ore, blister, or refined. In particular, problems having to do with semis entering into world trade are very complicated.

As compared to the trade in primary copper, there is very little movement of secondary copper across international boundaries. Export licensing is practiced in many countries, and to some extent there is an outright prohibition of scrap trade. The object of these restrictions is to reduce the need to import primary refined which, as pointed out in the next chapter, is often expensive relative to secondary, and thus to some extent to encourage the expansion of the industry producing secondary copper. The largest importer of scrap of all the major copper consumers is Japan, which gets much of this material from North America. An expanded scrap trade should also be the result of the abolishment of many trade barriers within the E.E.C. The situation in regard to the trade in scrap in 1968 is shown in table 3–6.

Table 3–6.   Imports and Exports of Copper and Copper Alloy Scrap (1968)

Importing Countries	EEC	OWE	EE	NA	OA	J	OAS	A	AU	U	Total
Exporter											
EEC Countries (EEC)	105,022	7,695		33		245					112,995
Other West Europe (OWE)	32,625	5,041		596		170					38,432
Eastern Europe (EE)	3,553	1,546				3					5,102
North America (NA)	99,954	10,142		69,936		38,197					218,229
Other America (OA)	2,758	203		2,751		574					6,286
Japan (J)	100			251							351
Other Asia (OAS)	6,814	827				16,894					24,535
Africa (A)	11,072	724				1,322					13,118
Australasia (AU)	393	25		116		602					1,136
Unknown Markets (U)	91	7									98
Totals	262,382	26,210		73,683		58,007					420,282

Source: International Wrought Copper Council Statistics.
Note: Units in metric tons.

Chapter Four

Secondary Copper

The purpose of this chapter is to discuss the supply and demand for secondary copper. Initially, however, I would like to show the flow of copper through an industrial economy in which copper can enter and leave the system through mine production, stockpiling, foreign trade, etc. The method of presentation is to construct vectors similar to "activity" vectors for what I term the mining, smelting, refining, and "rest of the economy" sectors, where this latter sector is effectively a final demand sector for copper. These vectors are given in physical terms, with the common unit being the copper content of the respective entry. I have also constructed Figure 4–1 (given later in this chapter) in order to show these same flows in a more direct form, employing values for 1965. These same values are employed in the discussion of the vectors, and the interested reader can locate these flows in both places. Similarly, Figure 1–1 should be consulted in conjunction with Figure 4–1, since in the former diagram certain important aspects of the flows through the system can be seen more clearly. (For instance, wire mills purchase only refined copper, while brass mills, foundries, and powder mills use both refined copper and various types of scrap.) Taking the smelting sector first we have:

(1)
Mine Production − Exports + Imports ± Stock Changes −
Direct Use of Concentrates + Secondary Blister =
Smelter Input $(= O_T - O_E + M_{OS} \pm \Delta O_L - O_I + I_S)$

In this expression the direct use of concentrates signifies the direct use of the copper concentrate in an industrial process (in the rest of the economy sector); while Secondary Blister is derived from scrap which, because of some undesirable properties, must go through the converter (and be "converted" into blister copper) before it goes to the refinery. The input-output scheme is as follows:

	O	S	R	I	F_E		F_L		T	
O		O_S		O_I	O_E		ΔO_L		O_T	
S										
R										
I		I_S								
M		M_{OS}								

The sectors here are mining (O), smelting (S), refining (R), and the rest of the economy (I). Final demand is F_E (Exports) and F_L (changes in inventories). M_{OS} signifies imports of ore into the smelting sector, and O_T is the total output of the mining sector. If we take S_{ST} as the input of the smelter, which in turn is equal to the flow through the smelter, which is also equal to smelter output—all in copper content—and assume negligible losses, we get from rewriting (1):

$$S_{ST} = I_S + M_{OS} + (O_T - O_E - O_I \pm \Delta O_L) = I_S + M_{OS} + O_S$$

where O_S is the output of the mining industry that continues to the smelter. Using U.S. figures for 1965, we have $S_{ST} = 85,200 + 33,400 + (1,229,000 - 9,700 - 0 - 8,300) = 1,329,600$. This value is also indicated in Figure 4–1. The next step is the construction of the input vector for the refining sector. For this we have the relationship:

(2)   Smelter Production − Exports (of smelter products) + Imports (of smelter products) ± Stock Changes + Refined From Scrap − Direct Use of Blister = Refinery Input ($= S_{ST} - S_E + M_{SR} \pm \Delta S_L + I_R - S_I$)

There are several items here that need clarifying. The entry "refined from scrap" (I_R) gives the copper content of old and new scrap that is an input for the refineries. It should be understood, however, that much scrap is not refined and goes directly into foundries, powder mills, brass mills, or other processes, without refining (see Figure 4–1). As for the "direct use of blister" (S_I), this simply indicates that there are industrial processes that take the blister direct from the smelter, without refining. The following tableau can now be constructed:

	O	S	R	I	F_E	F_L	T
O							
S			S_R	S_I	S_E	ΔS_L	S_{ST}
R							
I				I_R			
M				M_{SR}			

Here S_{ST} is the output of the smelter industry (measured in copper content), while M_{SR} gives the import of smelter products into the refining sector. We can then get by rewriting (2):

$$R_{RT} = I_R + M_{SR} + (S_{ST} - S_E - S_I \pm \Delta S_L) = I_R + M_{SR} + S_R$$

In this expression S_R is the output of the smelter industry that is an input to the refining industry. R_{RT} is thus the refinery input (and, given negligible processing losses, also refinery output). Going once more to the U.S. figures for 1965, we get R_{RT} = 318,700 + 301,700 + (1,329,600 − 4,400 − 0 + 11,200) = 1,956,800. Note that the positive sign for ΔS_L indicates a fall in the stock of blister. The final tableau is constructed of the following elements.

(3)   Refined Production (copper content) − Exports (refined) + Imports (refined) ± Changes in Inventories of Refined (private + official) = Total Consumption of Refined (= $R_{RT} - R_E + M_{RI} \pm \Delta R_L \pm \Delta R_G$)

And the tableau is:

	O	S	R	I	F_E	F_G	F_L	T
O								
S								
R				R_I	R_E	ΔR_G	ΔR_L	R_{RT}
I								
M				M_{RI}				

Here M_{RI} is refined copper imported into, what is for the copper industry, the final use sector. (The entries in this tableau can also be checked against Figure 4–1.) The final demand of the public authorities also shows up here through the change in government inventories. The input-output balance for the Total Consumption of Refined Copper (copper content) = $R_{RT} = M_{RI} + (R_{RT} - R_E \pm \Delta R_L \pm \Delta R_G) = M_{RI} + R_I$, and for the U.S. in 1965 this gave: $124,700 + (1,956,800 - 294,900 + 6,900 + 46,300) = 1,839,800$. It should be observed that in this case we have a fall in private and public inventories.

The preceding analysis has passed over unrefined scrap. In the world as a whole, in 1965, this involved about 2,040,000 metric tons. The amount of refined scrap was reckoned at 853,000 tons. Along with scrap in the form of blister, the total figure was about 3,200,000 tons. Given that total world copper consumption was set at about 8,200,000 tons in that year, it seems that scrap accounted for about 40 percent. This percentage would also seem to be about right for the U.S., at least in 1965, as the reader can see by examining Figure 4–1.

Secondary copper has always been important; in the future it may well be crucial. If, as certain people are beginning to say, a shortage of basic minerals must be reckoned with in the years to come, then the "mining" of scrap must be judged as one of the most important of all contemporary industrial activities.

Up to the present time, primary and secondary production have moved more or less in phase. The logic here is obvious: when the demand for primary copper is high, the ensuing price rise makes it profitable to increase production of secondary copper. Some evidence exists, however, that we are entering a period when the percentage of secondary copper (as a fraction of total copper) may be on the increase.

As mentioned earlier, a significant proportion of all copper used in the past is still in existence. The amount of this metal that is capable of being recycled at any given time is a function of many things, but it seems indisputable that the technology of the period, both in regard to the secondary metal industry *and* the forms in which secondary metal appears, is of great importance.

The early processes for recovering secondary metal amounted to little more than simple melting operations in which scrap metal constituents were blended together in rather primitive processes, with little or no intention expressed as to obtaining an output in any way comparable to primary copper. During this period a distinct line could be drawn between primary and secondary material. During World War II, however, higher grades of secondary copper began to appear as a result of the general shortage of primary metals. What resulted was not only a large increase in the production of secondary metal but a general increase in the acceptance of this metal. As the situation now stands, several categories of purchasers rate some grades of (unrefined) scrap as being almost identical to primary copper for their purposes. (Naturally, secondary material

Figure 4–1. Flow Diagram for Primary and Secondary Copper (U.S., 1965) Statistics of the World Bureau of Metal Statistics and U.S.

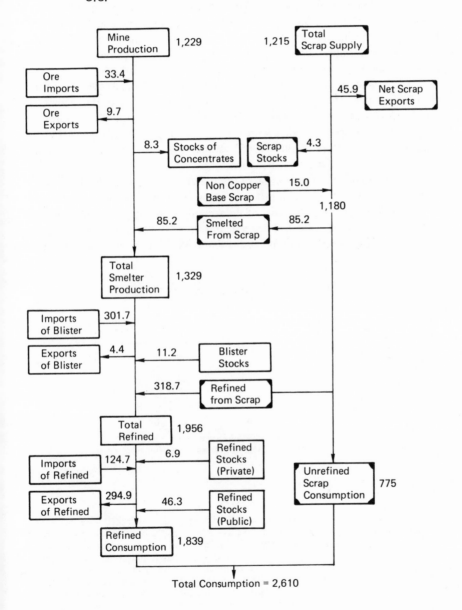

Source: Government Stockpile Reports. (In thousands of metric tons.)

that has gone through the refinery is almost indistinguishable from primary copper.) It is also true that increasing quantities of scrap are now being processed in primary smelting operations.

Some information is available about the amount of copper that is available in "finished" goods. This is not to say that all of it could be extracted by the application of present technology, but a large amount could, and future technology will undoubtedly be more effective.[1] Where the United States is concerned, Table 4–1 gives some idea of the situation up to 1968.

One of the conclusions that could be drawn from Table 4–1 is that given a sustained effort to develop and perfect the technology of the secondary metal industry, it may be possible for the U.S. to ignore much of that portion of the doomsday prognosis dealing with the exhaustion of primary copper. For the entire nonsocialist world, Grillo [1965] estimated in 1965 that the total amount of copper in use amounted to 60 million tons.

Where the classification of scrap is concerned, present listings in the U.S. contain about thirty-eight different types, most of which are compositions of brass and bronze. In 1967 most of the secondary copper produced originated in copper base alloys, as the following figures show. In the case of new scrap or scrap originating in production processes that could be termed current, we have:

Table 4–1. Scrap Accumulation (U.S.)

Year	Scrap Accumulation 1,000's of Short Tons
1940	14,735
1945	19,933
1950	24,169
1955	28,615
1960	32,630
1965	37,346
1968	40,333

Source: United States Bureau of Mines and Office of Mineral Resources Evaluation.

[1] One figure now being presented is 85–85 percent of locatable copper as the amount potentially recoverable from all uses, assuming both the continued development of recovery technology, and increasingly prohibiting the use of copper in those goods and processes where it cannot be recovered. We see immediately that we have a multiplier effect here—that is, M tons of copper can eventually be multiplied up to $M(1 + \phi + \phi^2 + \ldots \phi^i + \ldots) = M/1 - \phi$, where ϕ is the percentage recoverable. This figure, of course, would have to be considered in the light of the obsolescence cycles of the goods in which copper is used; but it seems clear, even now, that countries without substantial domestic sources of minerals are doing their citizens an enormous *disservice* by not paying a great deal more attention to their secondary metals industries.

New Scrap	*Short Tons*
Copper Base	667,080
Aluminum Base	10,000
Nickel Base	157
Zinc Base	11

As for old scrap:

Old Scrap	*Short Tons*
Copper Base	476,471
Aluminum Base	5,500
Nickel Base	623
Tin Base	50
Zinc Base	50

The total amount of scrap came to 1,159,907 short tons. As shown in Figure 4–1, total consumption of scrap came to 1,175,000 metric tons *minus* the export of refined scrap. (As far as I can tell, it is almost impossible to separate this exported refined out from the total exports of refined.) No great amount of space will be used here to examine the equipment and techniques that are found in the secondary copper industry, but a typical processing cycle is shown in Figure 4–2.

In conjunction with Figure 4–2 it should be pointed out that secondary refineries in the industrial countries generally have as an input a combination of scrap and blister. Of that part of scrap which does not go to refineries, a large proportion is made into brass, bronze, and other alloy ingots. There is also a certain amount of old scrap that is highly contaminated with all sorts of metals, especially tin, and which is sold to refineries where impurities are extracted and most of the copper is turned into ingots. Occasionally some of these impurities are marketable.[2]

In the developed market economies, about 22 percent of total refining capacity is used to refine secondary materials. At the present time this proportion may be increasing, since with refining capacity as a whole on the increase and growing concern being expressed about the future reliability of supplies from the less developed countries, it would hardly make sense not to increase this proportion—and to increase it as rapidly as possible.

The final point to be made in this section is the obvious one that the cost of producing one ton of secondary refined is almost always less than that of producing one ton of primary refined. In the production of primary copper the cost of mining, concentrating, and smelting account for a much larger percentage of total costs than the cost of refining, while on the basis of Figure 4–2 it is clear

[2] A number of important observations about secondary copper are to be found in Spendlove [1969].

Figure 4–2.   Processing of Secondary Copper

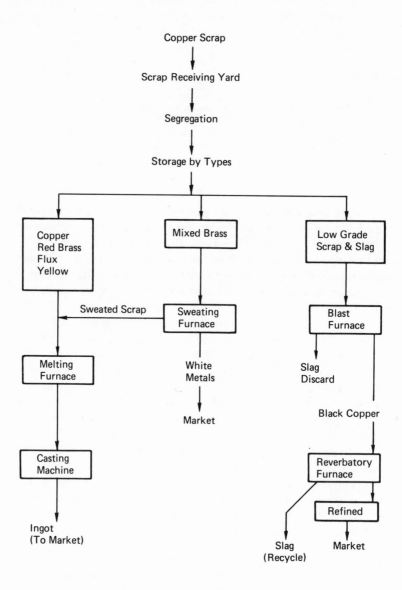

Source: Adopted from the UNIDO Document "Opportunities in the Production of Secondary Non Ferrous Metals," 4 September, 1969, by Max J. Spendlove.

that the steps leading up to the first stage of refining are simply collecting, segregating, and storage. According to some estimates, the cost of converting scrap into refined copper amounts to between 3 and 6 cents per pound, which at the present time is less than 10 percent of the price of refined copper.

PRICES

While overall price movements on the secondary market are similar to those on the primary market, it seems clear that fluctuations are milder on the former. Taking the British market as an example, the LME price index reached 240 in March 1968, while the indices for the various types of scrap varied from 184 to 211 at the same time.

In addition, the prices of the lower grades of scrap vary over a smaller range than the higher grades. This is to be expected since, with high grade scrap compositionally very similar to refined copper as far as some input structures are concerned, it seems reasonable that they exhibit similar price movements. Another point of interest has to do with the competitiveness of the secondary industry as compared to the primary. In almost all the major consuming countries, there are large numbers—sometimes hundreds—of secondary producers competing for scrap, where producers in this context means people who collect and sell scrap to a custom refiner. Their actions and reactions, in response to some variant of profit-maximizing behavior, probably work to dampen price movements.

At the same time it can be admitted that if scrap producers accumulate substantial inventories of copper, they will possess the potential to add a destabilizing element to copper prices, as a number of investigators and observers have pointed out. However, the same type of models that are used to demonstrate instability can, on the other hand, generate increased stability given appropriate values of the parameters of the model. The opinion here is that the key factor is the number of producers and the degree of association between them.

A partial support for this last assertion follows from the situation in 1965 when high prices resulted in greatly increased amounts of scrap being brought to market. Although secondary producers apparently understood that they were entering a period of high demand, their aggregate behavior was decidedly free of any speculative tendencies, and many refiners were able to buy large amounts of copper at sizable discounts. In addition, during this period scrap came to be regarded by many persons and organizations as the most reliable source of copper. This situation should be observed very carefully by the copper-producing countries, since what it could mean is that during downswings in copper consumption, it is the deliverers of secondary rather than primary copper who will be favored by consumers. Although the association of the oil-producing countries (OPEC) is often mentioned in the same breath as the association of copper-producing countries (CIPEC), their situation is fundamentally different. The oil producers do not contend with such a powerful rival.

Some time ago proposals were advanced, though only tentatively, that the time had come to exercise some control over the price of scrap. In particular, a kind of central buying and selling organization would be set up to "stabilize" the price of copper by purchasing when the price was down and selling when it was up. As it happened, the proposition never moved beyond the conference stage and, as far as I know, was generally opposed—both by producers and consumers of scrap. The argument most generally used against it was that, as opposed to primary copper, conditions on the secondary market approached a high level of "free" competition, and controls would be superfluous.

At the same time rumors continue to insist that a buffer stock for copper, on the order of the tin buffer stock, is to be set up. It seems to me that given the difficulties experienced with tin, an indirect approach might be worth considering for copper. This approach would have as its goal, however, not the so-called stabilization of price, since the real but unspoken purpose of most stabilization schemes is simply to accommodate the less developed countries by putting a floor on the price. Instead I would be concerned with the long-run ceiling—which I would try to maintain by subsidizing investments in secondary refining, "prospecting," and similar activities—to include research. The floor would be maintained by direct subsidies, and its level would be related to the general economic development in the relevant countries, rather than just the development of the copper industry.

Chapter Five

The Costs of Production:
A General Appraisal

As is readily apparent to the curious, there are various characteristics
of the copper industry that cause it to be distinguished from many primary
product industries. The first, and perhaps the most important, is size. Sir Ronald
Prain of Roan Selection Trust, perhaps the most eminent member of the international copper community, estimated that in 1967 the launching of a typical
mine with an annual capacity of 80,000 tons (with integrated smelting and refining facilities) required an initial investment of $120 million dollars; but a figure
that is sometimes used for the United States is about $2,000–$2,800 per ton for
new capacity. In addition, the expansion of existing mines requires an investment
of $1,200–$1,500 per ton of annual production. It should be pointed out, however, that the term typical, as employed above, undoubtedly had to do with
yesterday's technology. The new installation on Bougainville, which will mine
and process only 150,000 tons of copper per year, has an initial capital cost in
excess of $350 million.

When examining the feasibility of mining sites, a number of factors
are important. These include the copper content of the ore, the type of mining
operation (open pit or undergound), whether joint products are available (such as
gold, silver, nickel, etc.), and their value and abundance, and the running costs of
the operation.

In the United States most copper production (about 85 percent) is of
the open-pit variety. Since at present this process permits the exploitation of
ores containing as little as 0.5 percent copper, it can be understood why, with an
average grade of about 0.6 percent, United States copper can be considered
competitive. Moreover, it is estimated in certain circles that the average grade of
ore bodies being exploited in the U.S. in the 2000s will be in the neighborhood
of 0.25 percent (see Table 5–1).

It has been said that the lowering of the average copper content of
ores during the last seventy years has been responsible for about 50 percent of

Table 5–1.   Copper Content of Ore in U.S. (in Percents)

Year	1880	1902	1906– 1910	1911– 1920	1921– 1940	1941– 1950	1951– 1956	1970
Copper content	3.0	2.7	2.1	1.7	1.6	1.0	0.8	0.6

Source: UNIDO Documents (UNIDO, ID/WG 74/4, Somerset, G.S. "Economic Aspects of Copper Production and Marketing Possibilities for Developing Countries").

Table 5–2.   Copper Content of Ore in Zambia

Year	(1) Ore Hoisted (1,000 tons)	(2) Copper Produced (1,000 tons)	Ore Quality (2) / (1)
1954		346	
1955	15098	390	.026
1956	17660	435	.025
1957	18905	480	.025
1958	17519	441	.025
1959	22511	595	.027
1960	24971	635	.025
1961	23763	634	.027
1962	23431	620	.026
1963	25011	648	.026
1964	27388	697	.025
1965	30801	767	.025
1966	27750	687	.025

Source: Copper Industry Service Bureau (Zambia).

the price rise of copper. In fact, were it not for the technical progress in ore mining, dressing, concentrating, and some metallurgical processes, this percentage would probably be higher and, in addition, the price of copper higher, since in 1966–68 it was necessary to treat about 190 tons of ore to produce 1 ton of metal instead of the 40 tons that were treated early in the century.

Where other countries are concerned, Chilean ore grades usually run between 1 and 2 percent, while the Congo still has deposits with a copper content of 4 to 5 percent. In fact, initial drilling results by the international consortium Socotef (see Chapter 2) at the Tenke Fungurume deposits indicate an ore grade of over 6 percent, and there are indications that the initial operation may be of the open-pit variety. The grade in Zambia has run up to 4 percent, but, as the figures in Table 5–2 show, the average is about 2.5 percent.

In the rest of this chapter, attention will be paid, first of all, to the costs of producing copper and how these costs are distributed between prime costs, taxes, etc. Most of the operations examined will be in the less developed countries, and this will involve, to a certain extent, commenting on the interplay between the mining industry and economic development in these countries. These comments will be held to a minimum, however, since in my opinion economic development is a cultural rather than an economic or political problem. The question that will be touched on here has to do with who is going to control the mines—the governments of these countries or the mining companies. The answer to this question is, of course, that this control will very soon be completely in the hands of the local governments, although what they are going to do with it is quite another matter.

TRANSPORT COSTS

Some topics involving transport costs will now be examined. In the case of Africa, although wages are low and ore grades are probably the richest in the world, transport costs are extremely high. If we consider shipments from Katanga (Zaire) to Europe, about 80 percent of costs are incurred in the journey to the sea. These costs are expected to be reduced considerably, however, when the Tanzam railway is completed and the ore can be shipped direct to Dar Es-Salaam.

At the other end of the scale, wages are high in the U.S., but the transportation system has the capability to move raw ores or processed materials between producer and consumer with a high efficiency and at a moderate cost. Latin America falls about in the middle as far as ore grades and transport costs are concerned and, when the wage rate is taken into consideration, the mines of Chile and Peru are generally considered to have the lowest production costs in the world.

Where savings on transport costs are concerned, there is no question but that some cost reductions can be made if ocean transport costs can be reduced. One suggestion that immediately comes to mind involves increasing the capacity of ore carriers in the same dramatic way that the capacity of oil carriers has been increased. I have been assured, however, that it is just as costly to move (and store) too much copper as it is to move too little.

At the same time it is evident that there are considerable gains to be made if the world ocean routes were used more effectively. In a recent study of the trade flows of nonferrous metals, S.E. Tilton [1966] has provided some information that casts an interesting light on the way trade routes are being used. Tilton has employed the transportation model of linear programming to work out the optimal pattern of world trade for these metals, and he has shown that the actual pattern deviates considerably from this least cost ideal.

According to Tilton, the optimal trade pattern is being distorted by such things as ownership ties, political considerations, and the like. I don't believe that Tilton mentioned incompetence, but I am sure that had he thought of it, he would have included it.[1]

One of the solutions for this problem is to reduce the excess profits of the third party, the transporters of copper. A possible way of doing this is to develop a closer synchronization between sellers and buyers, so that inputs contracted for but not needed can be used elsewhere. This would also result in a reduction in inventory costs. At the same time, as more optimal sales and shipping paths are being worked out, compensatory payments could be made to producers or consumers who "lose" before the optimum pattern is obtained. These payments could be made as savings on shipping costs become available over other routes in the global trading network.

As far as this suggestion is concerned, it is interesting to note that the concept of "bankability" of copper is a first step toward developing trade patters having a higher degree of optimality. Perhaps the initial arrangements involving this concept were made because of steps taken by the large copper consumers, Japan and Germany, to secure sources of supply through the use of loans, direct participation, long-term contracts, or a combination of these devices. With these sources of supply located over the entire world, a number of possibilities exist to rearrange shipping patterns. For example, instead of shipping Bougainville concentrates to West Germany and Zambian blister to Japan, a swapping operation is arranged with the Zambian blister going to Germany and the concentrates to Japan. A similar arrangement took place in 1969 when a shipment from LME stocks to China was scheduled while, at the same time, Japan had contracted to make shipments to the LME. Instead the Japanese copper went to China, and the LME copper to a buyer closer to the U.K.

Bankability involves, in the language of the developers of this concept, a pool of "paper copper" that can be moved about with great facility. Ostensibly, the establishment of LME warehouses in the main producing and consuming areas would be a start to such a project. An argument could be forwarded, however, that sufficient storage facilities already exist at the places where copper is produced and processed. What is needed, instead, is a central computer installation with complete information on stocks, requirements, production, costs of production, quality, etc. This installation would calculate optimal shipment and cross payments in a manner similar to that employed by those airlines that have "pooled" facilities in order to avoid duplication. (It must be remembered, however, that the input structures of many processors are so rigid that they can only take inputs from certain sources. For instance, there are firms in Sweden that will only use copper from several mines in Chile, and I have

---

[1] As an example Tilton takes Rhodesia and the Congo. Rhodesia's actual shipment of copper to the U.K. in 1960–62 was 743.6, while the calculated optimal amount was 33.4. Similarly, actual shipments from the Congo to Benelux were 613, while the calculated optimal was 200.

been told that Phillips of Holland will only buy wirebars from Bolliden of Sweden. Of course, this type of specialization is, for the most part, a short-run phenomena, but it exists just the same.)

TAXES AND RELEVANT ALLOWANCES

Tax systems for the copper mining industry vary from country to country, and in some cases the rate of taxation may vary from mine to mine. Among the six major copper producers, Canada would appear to offer the most attractive fiscal arrangements—at least from the point of view of the individual private company. The U.S. also has a fiscal system designed to put the mining industry completely at ease. The Canadian system features a three-year tax holiday for new mines, very small indirect taxes, a company tax of 47 percent, and extremely liberal depreciation and depletion allowances. Similarly, the U.S. has taxed mining at a rate of 48 percent, and the generous depletion allowances make the effective rate considerably lower.

Until recently, Chile had a very attractive tax system. (Now, of course, with the mines nationalized, the previous arrangements are mostly of historical interest.) Among other things, this system was occasionally very effective from the point of view of getting a maximum output. During one period there was a special tax rate for each mine, with the highest rate approximately 53 percent. Indirect charges were hardly resorted to, but there was a penalty charge on exports of blister that could have been refined domestically. Depreciation allowances were designed to encourage a high production, in that high outputs permitted a very high rate of depreciation and thus, when prices were high, exceptionally generous profits. On the other hand, cutbacks in output were penalized through having a very low depreciation rate applied.

The tax system of Zambia comprises a mixture of direct and indirect taxes. There is a royalty for each ton of copper produced that is related to quotations on the LME. The formula that is used is 13.5 percent of the LME price minus $22.4 per long ton. This tax, and the export tax described below, is scheduled to be replaced by a mineral tax; however, the royalty as such is of some interest from an economic point of view, since it is probably a very inefficient tax. What it does is to levy a charge upon working costs rather than profits, which means that certain ore bodies which could be worked if this charge did not exist, must be abandoned. Among other things, this penalizes employment and, indirectly, the government: they lose revenue from the profits tax and any other tax they place on mining; they lose income tax from the personnel that would have been employed at the mine; they may have to pay unemployment benefits; and a certain amount of social unrest is generated. In addition, a royalty might bring about a situation in which ore bodies are bypassed or mines prematurely shut down. In the former case these ore bodies must often be assumed to be lost forever, while the cost of reopening a shut-down mine is sometimes so large that such an action is ruled out even if at a later date the royalty was removed and replaced by a subsidy of equal size.

The ideal levy in this industry is probably some sort of rent. This rent would be a function of the richness of the vein—that is, it would be lower for high cost mines than those with low costs, and it would be designed to remove some of the very high profits that occasionally appear in mining. It may be the case, however, that no single tax can accomplish this purpose, while at the same time maximizing output (and employment), and therefore more than one tax might have to be used.

There was also (in Zambia) an export tax of 40 percent of the LME price minus 336, where the units are U.S. dollars per long ton. This tax was formed so that when the LME price was less than $840, there was no tax. Obviously this device also discriminated in favor of low cost mines, but this is a minor point since it was intended to transfer as much revenue as possible to the government (especially revenue resulting from transient price increases) without diminishing the incentive to open new mines. The $840 can thus be regarded as a sort of cutoff point, above which it was felt that the mining companies were prepared to consider a new capacity. A brief examination of the balance sheets of the mining companies reveals that the revenue effect was, at least during the Vietnam boom, considerable; but as far as I can tell there were no extensive increases in planned capacity during this period. It should be noted that at least for public relations purposes, the mining companies occasionally indicated that they felt a suitable cutoff point was $900, although it is difficult for me to see how they arrived at this figure—particularly when the average cost of production in Zambia during 1968–69 appears to have been about $600 per metric ton.

The remaining component of taxation is a corporation tax of 45 percent on profits. There were also no depletion allowances or fiscal incentives to encourage the opening of new mines. It was true, however, that there were a number of cases of the Zambian government making rebates or refunds with an idea to equalizing the discriminatory effect of the export and royalties tax against higher cost installations. As mentioned earlier, the intention is to replace the latter two taxes by a mineral tax that will be treated as a cost of production, although it is to be calculated in terms of the profits of a company. This, together with the corporation tax, should get the total tax rate on profits up to about 73 percent, a figure that Sir Ronald Prain has noted in passing as ". . . high by world standards . . . ." Perhaps, but whether it is as high as it will be in the future is something we have to wait and see.

Zaire will be bypassed here, since the government has not, as far as I know, published a detailed account of the arrangements that are being worked out for the new foreign companies that are being allowed to participate in mining. Still it seems likely that the previous fiscal system, which was one of the most complicated in the mining world, has been modified considerably. This system included an exchange tax on the purchase of foreign exchange for the purchase of imports for the mining industry, a sliding scale of export taxes, a royalty of 10 percent, a turnover tax of 7.5 percent, a statistical tax, a sliding scale of profits taxes, plus a number of taxes classified as "miscellaneous."

Peru is not taken up at this point, although the reader will find information on the taxes paid by the mining companies in Peru in a later section of this chapter.

The final topic considered in this section is the depletion allowance, an item that has been mentioned several times earlier. This allowance was conceptualized as an analogy to the depreciation allowance—that is, it was intended to provide for capital recovery from a wasting asset in the same way that the depreciation allowance makes this provision for physical capital. In the U.S. depletion is based not on cost but on gross income. For copper mines the depletion allowance has been set at 15 percent: 15 percent of gross income is subtracted from net income in calculating the tax base.

In addition (also in the U.S.) extremely liberal capital gains provisions are available. A mining firm may take a lease on a possible site, develop it to the point of production, and then sell its interest and take advantage of the capital gains treatment of net revenue. This type of taxing, together with depreciation, intangible drilling and developing costs, interest on borrowed money, land development costs, overhead expenses, and the like have undoubtedly provided the mining sector with substantial incentives for exploration and high volume production. It has also provided the incentive for a number of people—some of whom have only a nominal association with the mining industry—to make a fool of the internal revenue service.

In fact, considering the tax favorization necessary to obtain the raw material inputs of the American industrial machine, perhaps the time has come to ask if there is not too much mining activity in the U.S. and perhaps too much smelting and refining in both the U.S. and the other industrial countries. Assuming that the base premises of the law of comparative advantage still apply, it is hard to see why a large-scale transfer of these activities to the less developed countries should not take place—assuming, of course, that the cost of this shift will not fall squarely on consumers such as myself. But even given this possibility, it seems to me that transfers of this type are a more suitable means for helping these countries expand their industrial structures than the direct financial transfers that constitute a large part of "development" aid at the present time, and which most evidence indicates to be a waste of time, energy, and money.[2]

---

[2]Except, of course, for those individuals on both ends who have managed to make their careers "channeling" aid and who, in fact, constitute a major obstruction to the industrialization and modernization of these countries.

LATIN AMERICA AND ZAMBIA

The topic of costs will now be put in historical perspective by examining some characteristics of the copper mining industry in Latin America and Zambia. The situation in South America is probably the most interesting if we go behind the scenes. In particular, the comic opera aspects of cultural conflict that are never far away when East meets West, or North meets South, were played out in a more leisurely setting, and patterns of corruption were in general more intricate. On the one side we observe a small group of technicians, living their expatriate lives of work, gossip, consumption, and petty intrigues; while on the other we have the local or indigenous population, which had about the same interests but not as much cash or energy to indulge them.

In Chile, the source of the conflict between the copper companies and the Chilean government centered on the question of "returned value," or that part of the revenues from mining that find their way into the hands of the local population—either as wages, taxes, payments for intermediate products, and so on. The Chileans claimed that this returned value was too low; while the copper companies, citing what they had come to think of as the magnificent services being rendered the country by foreign "venture capital," insisted that it was more than adequate. It should be stressed that this conflict over returned value existed almost from the moment of the first shipment of copper from Chile; and apparently no Chilean government, regardless of its political composition, was able to come to more than a temporary agreement with the copper companies as to what the rights and responsibilities of these companies were with regard to the disposition of their profits.

One of the things complicating the situation in Chile was the chronic disequilibrium of the economy as a whole. Despite industrialization, real wages seem to have been falling for a large part of the last twenty or thirty years. In addition, the high income groups developed a pronounced taste for imports, and it was not long before this taste had extended to every stratum of Chilean society. There was a constant and unremitting pressure on the balance of payments, considerable social unease, a corrosive climate of uncertainty that prevented the development of an adequate import substitution and noncopper export sector; and since various governments attempted to deal with these difficulties by printing large amounts of money and getting it into circulation as fast as possible, there was a very high rate of inflation.

In discussing these problems, one solution constantly returned to the tips of all tongues: first, increase the relative size of the returned value from the copper industry by increasing the taxes on these companies and increase its absolute value by increasing the total output of copper in Chile—or, put another way, increase the Chilean share of world copper production. This last goal was to be reached by increasing investment in the mines.

Here a problem was created that was only solved many years later through nationalization: if the government increased taxes, the copper companies refused to invest. They refused to invest in new capacity, and in addition replacement expenditure was reduced. Moreover, the government could not force them to invest, since the principal market for Chilean copper happened to be in the United States. Thus, had the mines been nationalized (prior to the availability of other markets) or otherwise interfered with in a manner deemed obnoxious by the copper companies, the government would have found itself with a larger problem on its hands than inadequate returned value: they would not have been able to sell what copper they were able to produce. Further, they probably would not have been able to produce any or, for that matter, been able to convince anyone else to produce it for them. In addition, the U.S. Marines were sometimes used to ensure that the concept of property rights was understood and given its proper respect in the Western Hemisphere, particularly when the property belonged to important firms with influence in the U.S. Congress.

For an economist examining all this, perhaps the most interesting problem is raised by the capital intensity of the copper industry. Wages in this industry are generally not a major part of costs, and if taxes are not extremely high, and the intermediate products required for production cannot be purchased from the local economy, an unusually large share of revenue disappears abroad. A part of this "unreturned value" could probably be regarded as legitimate by even Marxian standards; but there was a general belief that a large part of the time foreigners were taking home profits quite out of line with those that would have been available had the aspirations of the Chilean people been regarded more sympathetically—that is, *realistically.*

There was also the problem of technical change working to aggravate this situation. The average number of workers at Kennecott's El Teniente mine declined from 8,114 in 1931 to 6,978 in 1959, although production increased by about 70 percent. Employment at Anaconda's Chuquicamata mine showed a similar trend. Simultaneously, labor payments as a share of the value of production fell from about 20 percent in 1925 to about 16 percent in 1959. What this meant from the Chilean point of view was that the textbook argument that increases in foreign capital create employment became progressively difficult to accept. What Chile, as opposed to the large copper companies, needed was a labor-intensive industry which was also highly dependent on domestic intermediate goods. What they got was an industry that was highly capital intensive, becoming more so, and becoming even less dependent on local inputs due to the increasing technical sophistication of those inputs.

In itself, this could not be regarded as catastropic, since it could certainly be reasoned that increased mechanization of the mines made them more competitive. But under ideal circumstances, such as those presented in books and articles on development planning, a portion of the increase in the non-labor share would have been available for the expansion of employment elsewhere in the economy. Unfortunately, behavior of this sort is only seldom observed in reality, even under the most favorable of conditions, and therefore its absence is not surprising when the industry in question is foreign owned.

In June 1950, when the Korean War broke out, the U.S. government fixed the domestic price of copper at 24.5 cents per pound. This price was adopted by the U.S. companies in Chile as a kind of transfer price—that is, the price at which copper was to be valued for accounting purposes. Since the price of copper had been fixed during the second World War, with the result that the Chileans had lost several hundreds of millions of dollars in returned value, a wave of protest against this arrangement went up all over Chile. The U.S. government relented somewhat, increasing the price by three cents (which would accrue to the Chilean government), and also specifying that the Chileans could sell 20 percent of production at the "free" market price.

Even this arrangement was deemed prejudicial to Chilean interests; and what eventually happened was that the entire output of the Gran Mineria[3] was bought by the Chilean Central Bank (paying the fixed American price), and later resold for a price that was 10.5 cents higher. The result for the Chilean treasury was, of course, spectacular; and moreover a new precedent had been established in the relationship between Chile and the mining companies: that the government was prepared, if the occasion should present itself, to assume a certain responsibility for economic decisions being made on its territory.

At this point in the discussion, the question of taxes must be introduced. Up to the depression the companies paid a standard 6 percent tax, in addition to a 6 percent tax that had been levied in 1925. There was an additional 6 percent added in 1934, as the government attempted to compensate for revenues reduced by the continuing economic downturn. A special earthquake relief tax of 15 percent, designed to help finance the rehabilitation and development agency, appeared in 1939.

In 1942 another tax increase took place. With the copper price now officially fixed by the U.S. government at 12 cents per pound, this tax was designed to cut into any profits the mining companies might make by being able to sell at a price exceeding this fixed price, which was termed a base price. The new tax was fixed at 50 percent of any increase in profits, and this was increased to 60 percent in 1953. The mining companies responded to this by slowly but surely decreasing production whenever it was possible. Their position was, simply, that the Chilean government would have to change its tax policy if it wanted copper production in Chile to increase—that is, if they wanted further investment to take place in the mines. With the end of the war in Korea and a fall in the demand for copper, the logic of the mining companies prevailed. A so-called New Deal was drafted in 1955 calling for the levying of a single basic

[3]The term Gran Mineria is an official name for producers whose annual production is in excess of 25,000 tons of copper.

tax of 50 percent, which was to be supplemented by a variable tax that could reach 25 percent but which was decreased as production increased.

Other features of this agreement included a removal of the special exchange rate at which the companies had to buy local currency. (Just before introduction of the New Deal the "free" rate of exchange of the peso was 110 per dollar. The mining companies, however, received only 19.37 per dollar.) In addition there were incentives to invest in new refining capacity, one of which was granting the companies an allowance on all copper produced in new installations. Welfare expenditure for employees was made tax deductible; machinery imported to process indigenous raw materials was, to a certain extent, exempted from import duties; copper mined and then processed further in the country before export was exempted from the 25 percent variable tax; and so on.

According to Norman Girvan,[4] the policy did not work; and also, according to Girvan, it did not work because the copper companies acted in bad faith. No attempt will be made here to sit in judgment on either the mining companies, the government, or other economists, although in observing the international price trend for copper in the period of 1955–60, I am led to believe that conditions could hardly encourage investment. It is also possible that the more astute among the Gran Mineria executives had begun to see the handwriting on the wall. Yet, as Table 5–3 indicates, there was not exactly a stagnation in investment in the period of 1955–59.

Table 5–3.   Gross Investment in the Gran Mineria: 1922–64

Period	Investment (U.S. Dollars)
1922–24	40.1
1925–29	69.5
1930–34	7.1
1935–39	5.8
1939–44	12.0
1945–49	33.9
1950–54	115.0
1955–59	168.6
1960–64	82.5
1955–64	251.1

Source: *Cobre: Antecedentes Economicos Y Estadisticos Relaciona Dos Con La Gran Mineria Del Cobre, Officina De Informaciones Boletin De Informacion Economica No. 157,* Santiago, 1969.

[4]See Girvan [n.d.] for the full although hardly unbiased story of the adventures of Anaconda and Kennecott in Chile.

These investments did not, in any event, succeed in capturing for Chile the share of world output to which they believed themselves entitled. Other complaints against the mining companies were also registered during this period: in particular, that they had been able to avoid a part of the variable tax through an increase in capacity utilization, rather than by building out capacity, as had been the intention of the government. Also, refined production was not being expanded at the desired rate.

In 1960 the New Deal was abandoned, and new taxes imposed on the Gran Mineria. These new taxes pushed the rate on some of the mines up to 79 percent. In exchange the companies handed the government its conditions for an expansion program involving $500 million and a 40 percent increase in capacity. Included among these was a guarantee that the taxation and exchange arrangements of the New Deal would remain unchanged for twenty years. The issue was decided four years later when Senor Frei won the Chilean election and announced plans to buy out the mining companies. Later, when the Allende government came to power, these companies were simply taken over, or nationalized.

The result of this nationalization was that the struggle over returned value finally came to an end. The mines and all their assets were finally Chilean property. In the course of this transfer several interesting figures were quoted as to the value of the assets of the various companies. In the discussion about how much the Frei government should pay Kennecott for part of its Chilean subsidiary (the Braden Copper Company), the book value of these assets was placed at $66 million, while Kennecott insisted that the market value was $200 million. Eventually a price of $160 million was agreed upon.

Information at my disposal indicates that net income for the Braden Copper Company for the period 1955–64 was $163 million. If we take as the value of assets the $160 million which was the negotiated value, it would appear that these assets were generating a net return of about 10 percent—a figure which is about twice the value of the average yield on a share of the company's common stock during the last ten years. Almost one-third of Kennecott's production of copper was taking place in Chile in 1964, and this copper seemed to be contributing about 20 percent of net income to the company; however, if the book value of Chilean assets was indeed about $66 million, and the book value of all physical assets (in 1964) was $462 million, it would appear that Chilean assets were of an unusually high productivity. (This conclusion is reinforced by an apparent tendency of the company during the period of 1954–64 to keep physical investment to a minimum, holding almost 40 percent of its assets either in cash, bank deposits, bonds, and portfolio investments in other companies, and maintaining one of the most liberal dividend policies in the U.S.) The question that must now be asked is how much of this productivity is due to the company being able to transfer copper to the U.S. at a low bookkeeping price for further processing? If and when this question is answered, we can evaluate the figure of

$160 million at which the Braden Company was to have been compensated; without it all judgments are subjective. Even so, my opinion is that the Chilean government made an excellent arrangement—even if full compensation is paid.

There is a sequel to this story. *Newsweek* Magazine, March 13, 1972, published a short piece in which they noted that the Anaconda Company had been "decimated" by the nationalization in Chile and Kennecott badly hurt. Certain figures were also published to which the term irrelevant can probably be applied. (Relevant is the fact that the *Engineering and Mining Journal* reported in its February 1972 issue that Chile owed Kennecott $92.9 million and Anaconda $175 million).

Now in those pseudo-intellectual circles where many of us spent our formative years, we were always assured of two things: (a) the inability of the weekly newsmagazines to find or to recognize the truth and, in the unlikely event this did happen, to describe it meaningfully; and (b) the woe that could be expected to descend upon any American or European "multicontinental" firm losing that part of its operations located in an underdeveloped country.

About 50 percent of this youthful knowledge still applies. According to *Fortune* Magazine's Directory of the 500 largest U.S. industrial firms (*Fortune,* May 1973) and the balance-sheet-type information presented there, Anaconda—which had by far the largest involvement in Chile, both in terms of its operations there and its total operations—appears to be on its way to becoming one of the most profitable corporations in the U.S. Kennecott seems to be doing less well, but I have yet to meet anyone who believes that any difficulties it is experiencing are fundamentally related to its experiences in Chile during the last few years.

And last but not least, in the period between the submission of the final draft of this book and receipt of the copyedited manuscript, the Allende government has been replaced by the Military. What happened, quite simply, was that several groups in the ruling party decided that their personal struggle for control of the Chilean economy (to include the copper mines) was too important to delay until Dr. Allende consolidated his power. The result of this struggle was the weakening of the economy to a point where a civil war, or a putsch, was inevitable.

As was noted in Table 2–7, the Chilean copper industry had planned to increase its output by almost 500,000 tons in the near future; instead, because of strikes and other problems, production has been slowly falling. The opinion here is that the new rulers of Chile will spare no effort to see that this projected increase takes place, and they will probably have some success.

Welcome has also been extended anew to foreign investment. Just what this means is unclear at the present moment, but I hardly think that either Anaconda or Kennecott feel themselves included in this invitation, at least just now.

ZAMBIA

The copper mining industry of Zambia permits a more straightforward analysis than that of Chile. It begins with the presence of a large international demand for copper due to the rapid pace of industrialization in Europe and North America, and a completely new technology being imported to exploit the rich deposits of copper in the country. This technology consisted of large amounts of capital goods, European technicians and administrators, European skilled and, to some extent, semi-skilled workers, and African unskilled workers.

The situation developed as follows. In the beginning the arrangement with European skilled and African unskilled workers was regarded as immutable. When the African labor supply stabilized, however, largely through increases in wages and a wider recruiting of married workers, very large increases in the efficiency of these workers were made, and training schemes for Africans resulted in still further increases.

At the same time that increases in wages were taking place for Africans, similar advances were being recorded by Europeans. These changes are shown in Table 5–4, and the result was that the management of the mines not only began thinking the unthinkable but they began doing it: in the semi-skilled and to a certain extent skilled job categories (such as truck driver, blaster, underground locomotive operator, etc.) Africans began to replace Europeans.

Behind this table there is an interesting illustration of the factor substitution theory of elementary economics. To begin with, if wage *ratios* are calculated, it would appear that there would be an advantage in increasing the

Table 5–4.   African and European Money Wages: 1935–60

Year	African Wage	European Wage	Year	African Wage	European Wage
1935	10	431*	1948	30	562
1936	14	431*	1949	33	562
1937	12	431	1950	36	562
1938	12	431*	1951	43	716
1939	13	431	1952	50	855
1940	13	431	1953	74	1040
1941	15	431	1954	76	1040
1942	17	462	1955	80	1040
1943	18	462	1956	82	1040
1944	19	462	1957	121	1040
1945	19	462	1958	133	1143
1946	20	462	1959	138	1176
1947	20	539	1960	140	1281

Source: Year Book, 1955–60, Northern Rhodesia Chamber of Mines, Annual Report of the Department of Labour, 1935–54, Northern Rhodesia, Ministry of Labour and Mines.
* Estimated.

number of Europeans relative to Africans. This impression is wrong, however, since the gain in efficiency by the Africans was apparently at least as large as the relative increase in their wage. In fact, this augmentation of efficiency made it possible to increase mechanization by a certain degree, but not to take advantage of the full scope of mechanical techniques available to the mining industry at any given time. For instance, equipment requiring a great deal of servicing could not be profitably employed on the Rhodesian copper belt since, although the management of the mining companies had instituted a certain amount of on the job training for Africans, they had not established facilities for turning local workers into technicians. (The copper companies should probably not be criticized too strongly for this, however, since the record of the Zambian government is only marginally better.) Copper belt technicians were Europeans; they cost money, and management was encouraged to rationalize their use. At the same time technical changes of a certain type—in particular, those complementary with the existing skill level of Africans—were rushed into service. As it turned out, many of these improvements were labor saving, and they tended to increase the ratio of Europeans to Africans. The principal reason for this seems to have been that they reduced the number of underground workers faster than those working above ground, and since the ratio of Europeans to Africans was lower underground, they displaced proportionally more Africans than Europeans.

By 1953 African wages were rising considerably faster than equipment prices, and extensive rationalizations involving African workers were put into effect. It was not until 1955 or later, however, that the managers of copper companies were able to perceive that optimal rationalizing involved replacing a part of the high wage European work force by Africans. That this could be done was made clear by the situation in neighboring Katanga, where the European/ African ratio was much lower than in Rhodesia. After some complicated negotiations that had very little to do with economics, but very much with politics and social attitudes in Central Africa, a number of European jobs were "Africanized." The result of this, interestingly enough, was probably to decrease the total number of Africans employed in the mines. As Africans were trained to operate and to service equipment of a more complicated nature but at the same time received a wage for doing so that was much less than that of the European who had previously done this work, it became possible to put more of this equipment into operation. The mining industry, on the whole, became more mechanized; and at the same time some interesting discoveries were made concerning the work capacity of individual miners: this seemed to have increased due to the presence of a kind of Horndal or Learning-by-doing effect.[5] Unfortunately, output/head statistics do not appear to be usable beyond the first year of the "Zambianization" program (1965–66), but according to Table 5–5 it would not

[5]See Lundberg [1962] and Arrow [1962].

Table 5–5.   Output, Employment, and Productivity in the
Rhodesian Copper Industry (1954–66)

Year	Output in Thousand Tons	Employment	Output per Head (Tons)	Growth of Output per Head in Percent
1954	387.55	46.55	8.33	
1955	433.95	45.17	9.61	15.37
1956	495.64	47.82	10.36	7.80
1957	524.63	48.85	10.74	3.67
1958	484.29	41.95	11.54	7.45
1959	643.34	44.56	14.44	25.13
1960	679.75	46.62	14.57	0.90
1961	679.75	48.94	13.84	−4.67
1962	674.39	47.75	14.12	1.66
1963	715.97	46.88	15.27	8.14
1964	755.92	47.87	15.79	3.41
1965	834.70	49.25	19.95	7.35
1966	747.11	50.67	14.74	

Source: Copper Industry Service Bureau Year Books, Zambia.

appear that the new employment policy (the first stage of which was instituted about 1955–56) caused any serious disruptions of production.

By 1965 the time had come for the mining companies in Zambia (formerly Northern Rhodesia) to face up to what Prime Minister MacMillan had called the "winds of change." Translated into everyday language, this meant nationalization. As it happened, the results of nationalization were not as drastic as the managers of the companies had probably imagined in their speculations— or possibly their nightmares.

The reason for this is that while it was possible for the Zambian government to take over the mines, they were not able to organize their operation. Unfortunately, speechmaking and the efficient management of large industrial enterprises are not the same thing, for had it been possible to mine copper with rhetoric, the Zambians could have taken over 100 percent of the mines immediately, expelled the management and European workers, and put the very large profits then being made in the industry to work developing the economy—assuming, of course, that this is where these profits are intended to go.

As it was, they took control of 51 percent of the assets of the mines, at a price of $292,600,000—which was the book value of these assets on 31 December 1969. Arrangements were also finalized for a management and consultancy contract between the mining companies and the Zambian government.

By the time signatures had been applied to all documents, the stock markets in New York and London had finished making their adjustments, and share prices were more or less maintained. Compensation (for the Zambianized assets) was made in bonds carrying a coupon of 6 percent, and the market immediately discounted these bonds by 40 percent. The share market valuation of the transferred assets, however, appears to be considerably lower than the book value; and since by the admission of the managers the mechanization of the mines was lagging by at least ten years, it is a moot question as to whether bond-holders should consider themselves severely inconvenienced by the turn of events.

At the present time the share of Zambian copper in total world output seems to be falling, and assuming that Chilean and North American plans for expansion are not too drastically altered, this may continue to be the case. The problem of Zambia, as I see it, is one of training a class of technicians and administrators who can operate and expand the mining sector and use it as a base for general industrial and agricultural development. But what seems to be happening is that, for a good many years in the future, the government will have to be content with having the operation of the mines in expatriate hands while they play the part of rentier. A socialist rentier, of course.

PERU

The story of copper mining in Peru is similar to that for Chile. An interesting paper on the mining industry has been written by Claes Brundenius [1972][6] in which he catalogues the various unpleasantries visited on Peru by the large mining companies operating in that country. As it happens, I don't belong to the school of thought that considers imperialism by individual corporations to be a matter for serious contemplation—especially in these days when a call by such companies for gunboats simply results in the phone being hung up on the other end. As I see it, the large European and American corporations are able to abuse their position in underdeveloped countries because they happen to be able to solve the technical and administrative problems involved in exploiting the resources of these countries, while the indigenous population, particularly their so-called educated class, either cannot or will not.

Even so it is of some interest to reproduce the accounts showing the cost structure of the Southern Peru Copper Company, since these accounts for their Peruvian operation appear to be quite distinct from any activity they (or their mother company) might be undertaking elsewhere. Moreover, this company mines only a very small amount of gold and silver in addition to copper.

If costs are summed exclusive of taxes and this value subtracted from sales, we get a more conventional value for gross profits. With the given amount of taxes, we get an effective tax rate on profits of 54 percent. In addition, it appears that given the level of other expenditures, the Peruvian government (unlike that in Chile) was not especially interested in returned value.

[6]For a description of copper mining in a situation of extreme underdevelopment, the reader should consult Treadgold [1971]. Both this and the Brundenius paper contain excellent balance-sheet-type information.

What the figures in Table 5–6 indicate most of all, however, is the limited role that a highly capital-intensive industry such as mining can play as a direct generator of economic growth for the rest of the economy. The fuels and machinery required for the industry were almost certainly imported, and since mining equipment is probably increasing in complexity, this will most likely be the situation for an indefinite period in the future (and the same can undoubtedly be said for Zambia and Zaire). Similarly, it seems unlikely that the industry would be able to generate a large amount of pecuniary external economies in the form of a training effect for the labor force as a whole—although it is almost certainly the case that the lack of potentialities here is a function of the deficiency of imagination of policy-makers rather than the intrinsic limitations of the industry.

The copper industry in a poor country thus tends to be a mixed blessing where overall economic development is concerned, particularly if it is allowed to impose its own logic on the remainder of the economy. On the one hand, it gains valuable foreign exchange and makes possible the import of inputs that are indispensible to growth, and it certainly has an important training effect for those workers in the industry. But on the other hand, its high capital intensity tends to create a wage level that is quite out of line with the rest of the economy. (In Chile, for example, the wage of some workers in the mines is as

Table 5–6.   Cost Structure of the Southern Peru Copper Company, 1969 (in Millions of Soles)

Item	Amount	Amount (in Percent)
Wages	232	3.6
Salaries	257	3.8
Materials and equipment	790	12.2
Energy	213	3.3
Peruvian taxes	1,841	28.2
Royalties		
Amortization and interest	134	2.0
Sales costs	125	1.9
Other costs	97	1.5
Total costs	3,689	
Other deductible items		
Depreciation	444	6.8
Reserves		
Depletion	881	13.5
Costs + "deductibles"	5,014	76.7
Total sales	6,530	100.0
Sales costs (cash flow)	2,847	43.6
Net profit	1,516	23.3

Source: Brundenius 1972.

much as ten times the wage of factory workers in some of the most important industrial enterprises in the country.)

The result of this type of situation is that union and other pressures force the general wage level up, particularly in the urban areas. This tends to reduce or prevent the overall expansion of employment or, in cases where this cannot happen for one reason or another, leads to a severe inflation. (It is not unknown that both these things happen at the same time). Problems also arise due to an increase in the urban population caused by the presence of high wages but at the same time a stagnation of employment. Another possibility is that production in the rural (or traditional) sector expands in such a way as to dampen the forces encouraging growth—that is, the traditional sector expands slowly in response to demand pressures from the industrial sector, thus raising the price of traditional goods (for example, foodstuffs) and in the longer run elevating the standard of the rural population in such a way that the cost of transferring labor to the industrial sector progressively increases. (A simplified discussion of this problem is taken up in Appendix C.)

There is also the problem caused by the greater costs of training individuals to work in capital-intensive industries, and the disproportionate amount of economic power then held by these persons as compared to employees in the more labor-intensive occupations. This, by the way, usually causes a conflict that is resolved by still further wage increases to the latter group, which not only increases the misallocation of resources but leads to an intensifying of the inflationary pressures with which most economies of this type have to contend.

Chapter Six

Prices, Policy and Some General Observations on the World Copper Market

The first topic to be taken up in this chapter concerns a phenomenon of considerable importance in the United States: the two-tier pricing system, where the two tiers are composed of producers and merchants. This discussion is to a considerable extent about the competitiveness of the copper industry in the U.S., but certain points will be touched on that apply to the other principal consuming countries.[1]

As should be clear by now, this market can be characterized as a highly developed oligopoly, one of the most distinctive peculiarities of which is that the producer price is not an equilibrium price—not even, it appears, in the long run.[2] It is generally believed that the equilibrium price is considerably higher, since on the merchant (or dealer) market where fairly large amounts of copper are sold, the price has averaged about 35 percent above the producer price. Producers are apparently resorting to extensive rationing.

Three reasons can be given for producers not raising prices. The first is that higher prices might drive certain customers out of the market. As long as profits are satisfactory, producers apparently prefer to maintain existing relationships with established customers than to go for the top dollar. In a sense, this is a way of rewarding loyalty, since during the copper surplus of 1962–63 a number of fabricators abandoned the major producers to seek cheaper sources of supply. Many of these defectors must now stand at the rear of the line when copper is scarce.

The second reason has to do with forestalling substitution. High prices undoubtedly intensify the search for substitutes, and given the present

---

[1] An interesting and important article that deals with competitiveness in the world market is Stewardson [1970].

[2] By equilibrium price it is meant the price that would bring flow supply and demand into equilibrium (that is, current production equal to current use).

rapid advance of technology, an intensified search should prove to be of considerable danger for the industry. Most important, this situation is understood and its seriousness appreciated in fairly wide circles. Finally, of a less substantive nature, the U.S. government has from time to time followed a policy of holding prices down by selling from its stockpile. This discouraged investment and an expansion of output and, to a certain extent, taught producers how to live with lower prices.

Where rationing is concerned, it should be noted that there are undoubtedly less efficient methods for allocating resources, particularly if the rationer places the overall efficiency of the economy above his personal relations with the firm or individual seeking the commodity he is selling. Unfortunately most ordinary people do not act in this manner, and so the determining factor as to who is going to get how much usually turns out to be the historical relationship of supplier to suppliee. Some fabricators of demonstrably low efficiency have found themselves getting supplies of copper when it obviously would benefit society if these supplies were going elsewhere. This is so in that the concept of ideal allocation is based on resources going to where they have their highest value, and it is apparent that a low cost firm can bid more for a particular resource than one whose costs in other respects are generaly high. On this point one can note further that many high efficiency facilities have had to shut down for varying periods of time because they were not favored by rationers.

Rationing has also caused an effect on long-run supply that is of dubious value to the economy. The lower-than-market-price policy prevalent among producers has discouraged sustained investment in new sources of supply, since much investment in this industry is a function of the profits of the company in question. In fact it appears that the failure of supply to match demand after so many years of imbalance is one of the reasons why President Nixon established a commission, under the leadership of Professor Houthakker, to investigate the industry. Although the commission has issued a preliminary report, it is still too early to say just what the result of their various meetings and deliberations is going to be; however, the U.S. copper industry has apparently declared itself to be "not impressed" by the commission's activities, and since Houthakker recently returned to academic life, I think we can safely draw the conclusion that things will continue as before—at least for the time being.

The position of fabricators in the face of all this is as follows: unless they happen to be very large and influential or integrated forward with producers, they find themselves purchasing copper at varying prices. Stewardson has emphasized two prices in this context: the primary producers' price, and the custom smelters' price. The primary producers' price is for the most part related to refineries that are a part of a vertically integrated operation. (Or, simply, it is the price to which most copper sold by the large producers in the U.S. is related.) as Figure 6—1 indicates, this price is fairly stable, having a tendency to move up and down in "steps."

The custom smelters' price is quite naturally more volatile and is used by refineries buying their inputs on a less systematized basis—both in regard to source and price. It is the case, however, that in the U.S. many independent fabricators find themselves dealing with five or six prices. In addition to the U.S. producers' price, it is possible to cite the U.S. dealers' (or merchants') price, which corresponds to the custom smelters' price, the LME spot price, the foreign producers' (Congo-Chile-Zambia) price based on an LME price, and the price of numbers 1 and 2 scrap. These are shown in Figure 6–1.

By employing information published in the most authoritative trade journals, in particular the *American Metal Market,* it is easy to deduce that during the period 1963–69 most independent producers were buying less than 50 percent of their copper at the U.S. producer price. The basis for determining just how much of this comparatively low priced copper they could get was, as indicated above, the amount they purchased during the "bear" years of 1962–64.

The price of numbers 1 and 2 scrap are important because, for many purposes, they are very close substitutes for refined copper. (In fact, they differ from refined largely in shape and not in chemical composition.) It is also interesting to know that until about October 1965 the Congo-Chile-Zambia price moved in much the same way as the U.S. producers price. This arrangement was altered somewhat in 1964–65 when the African producers increased their price by a

Figure 6–1. Various Approximate Copper Prices from Around 1964 to About 1969

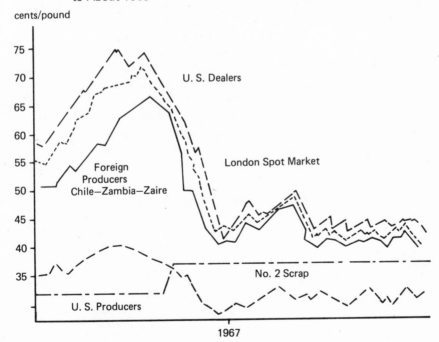

Source: American Metal Market and Engineering and Mining Journal.

small amount, but in October 1965 these three countries abandoned so-called producer pricing and went over to the LME three-month forward price.

The reason they left the producer price was because with the intensification of American engagement in Vietnam, it lagged far behind the LME price; and the reason they chose the forward instead of the spot price is because, they said, it displayed a greater stability. There have been a number of prices used by these producers since that time, almost all of them related to an LME price. This includes the *Engineering and Mining Journal's* Foreign Average (or Export Price) and the Union Miniere Price.

COPPER, ELECTRICITY, AND SUBSTITUTION

Although copper has many uses, its most important application continues to be within the electrical industry. The reason for this is its high electrical and thermal conductivity, its high resistance to corrosion, and its high malleability, ductility, and tensile strength. Moreover, its properties can be improved through alloying with other metals. Table 6–1 shows the use patterns of copper in the U.S. and France, by industry.

Aluminum is also a material that holds great promise for conducting electricity. It has about 60 percent of the electrical and thermal capacity of copper while weighing about a third as much. On the basis of the 1967 price levels for copper and aluminum wire, W.O. Alexander [1967] has calculated that the conduction of a certain amount of electricity by copper is four times as expensive, in terms of *metal costs,* as conduction by aluminum.

Up to the present time the use of aluminum in some high tension overhead transmission lines has been the most important gain for aluminum over copper in the electrical field, although other encroachments loom. Since 1964, for instance, aluminum has been making some headway in low tension lines both above and below ground. In addition, a composite copper-aluminum wire has recently been developed that may hold great promise for the generating of electrical energy, underground high tension lines, and in particular interior wiring. Where interior wiring is concerned, aluminum has a tendency to form an

Table 6–1. Copper Use by Industry: U.S. and France

Industry	U.S. (1971)	France (1970–71)
Electrical	55%	28%
Construction	10%	23%
Consumer durables	15%	9%
Transport	7%	10%
Industrial equipment	6%	10%
Other	7%	21%

Source: CIPEC: "Copper in 1972."

oxide on its surface that resists the flow of electricity, and in addition electrical contacts tend to heat up. The electrical grade of aluminum is also very soft, and under prolonged pressure (as in a terminal connection) tends to give, damaging the contact and causing more heat. There are apparently aluminum power lines in the U.K. that experienced this situation.

The composite wire, however, is reputed to avoid these difficulties, and it is said that savings as high as 30 percent are possible. Another factor of great importance in resisting the substitution of aluminum for copper has been the cost of installing aluminum wires, as well as some problems of safety connected with its use. But as a result of the sharp price rises experienced during the war in Vietnam, there was a feeling in certain consumer circles that copper was on its way to becoming a rare metal, and it might be wise to start thinking about its replacement. The long-run consequences of this type of reflection are too obvious to be gone into here, and this is particularly true in the light of the fact that the international market share of copper, as compared to aluminum, has already fallen from 90 percent in the 1930s to less than 50 percent today.

In examining the price series for aluminum and copper over the past fifteen or twenty years, I find it impossible to assemble a clear-cut argument in support of the claim that relative price ratios have consistently moved in favor of aluminum during this period.[3] It is difficult to sort out all the factors underlying the progress made by aluminum, since while there have been serious shortages of copper from time to time, short-run fluctuations of aluminum prices have often been more severe than those of copper. Among other things it seems to me that we might have a situation here analogous to that existing in the wool market, where technological progress has been accompanied by strenuous promotional

---

[3] Beginning with the relative price of copper to aluminum from 1946 to 1966 (21 observations) we see the following pattern for sign changes: $+ - - + + - + + + + - - + -$ $- + + 0 - +$. With slashes indicating the crossovers I get $+ / - - / + + / - / + + + + / - - / + /$ $- - / + + / - / + $. Assume the number of runs to be asymtopically normally distributed under the assumption of randomness, with mean and variance given by:

$$E(R) \approx \frac{n}{2} + 1 \qquad\qquad Var(R) \approx \frac{n(n-2)}{4(n-1)} \approx \frac{n-1}{4}$$

where n is sample size, and R the number of runs (where the number of runs is the number of blocks separated by slashes). I thus have $E(R) = 21/2 + 1 = 11.5$, and $Var(R) = 20/4 = 5$.

Prob. Value $= Pr(R \leqslant 11)$

$$= Pr \; \frac{R - u_R}{\sigma_R} \leqslant \frac{11 - 11.5}{\sqrt{5}}$$

$$= Pr(Z \leqslant 0.224) = 0.40$$

There would seem to be a strong possibility of randomness. My conclusion is that there is insufficient evidence to claim a trend in the ratio of copper to aluminum prices.

efforts on the part of the producers of substitutes. Another not entirely uninteresting facet of this problem is that in the U.S. a few of the most important fabricators of copper are also active in aluminum, and are not at all reluctant to suggest the replacement of copper by aluminum when it appears that they will gain some advantage from doing so.

Table 6-2 presents some information on the way substitution has progressed with electric cables in the U.K. and insulated lines and cables in France.

It should be apparent that these figures cannot be considered reassuring for the copper industry—although I am not sure whether we consumers should feel depressed by them. Some opinions have it that the development shown in this table will not continue, but the question of interest is what will happen if this trend spreads to other high consumer countries.

Outside the electrical field, copper is also strongly threatened by aluminum and, to a certain extent, plastics. Copper tubing, for example, can often be replaced by plastics, and during the price explosion of copper in 1966–70, plastics probably made some gains that are irreversible. Another problem for copper at the present time is the growing emphasis on the suppression of pollution, a certain amount of which is generated by the industry. It would appear, however, that much of the criticism of environmentalists on this point has been taken seriously, and new installations are being designed to give as little offense as possible.

In the automotive field, the retreat of copper continues unabated. Because the substitution of plastic or aluminum does not alter safety features, due to the small amount used per vehicle, and because there is no corrosion problem of the type to be found in ships, a mass defection from copper is not inconceivable. Thus far it would appear that sales to the automotive sector have been maintained because of the large annual increase in the number of vehicles, which have compensated to some extent for the inroads made by substitution. Whether this situation can be projected into the future depends upon whether plastics regain the momentum they apparently had a few years ago, when they were expected to be in the forefront of the next "Shumpeterian" new-product cycle. In any event, pipes, fittings, and other movable and semi-movable items that

Table 6-2.   Aluminum as a Percentage of Total Use

Country	1965	1966	1967	1968	1969	1970	1971
United Kingdom (Electric cables)	9.0	14.3	15.8	16.0	15.5	17.8	20.4
France (Insulated lines and cables)	7.2	13.7	16.1	16.4	19.3	20.7	22.8

Source: CIPEC reports, especially "Copper in 1972."

require extensive adjustment and complicated repairs will probably be less at home in such things as the automobile, central heating equipment, and plumbing of the future. This will almost certainly give more scope to plastics, since plastics permit such items as piping to be designed as an integral part of certain types of structural components, motor blocks, etc.

Some modifications of the above discussion should be offered to the extent that the automobile of the future might be an entirely different thing from that of today. Today's automobile uses about 35 pounds of copper, but if the automobile of tomorrow is going to be an electrical or steam-driven vehicle, it might have a much higher or lower copper input. I have not been able to get any information on the direction in which this input is liable to move, but it is an interesting observation that copper consumption in this case could be altered by finding a substitute for the final product in which copper is used, rather than by finding a substitute for copper itself.

It should also be remembered that aluminum and plastics are safer, politically, than copper. There is more aluminum than copper in the crust of the earth's surface, and as yet the main consuming countries have not had any extensive disagreements with its producers. This situation could, of course, change, but whether it does or not depends to a considerable extent on the scarcity of the commodity. As for plastics, these involve for the most part the domestic resources of the consumers, namely, skilled labor and technology. As a result, annoyances such as nationalization need not be taken into consideration.

On the other side of the ledger we can cite as working for copper the simple process of economic growth. There is a definite pattern of copper consumption as we move across the spectrum of development (measured in income per head), and it seems clear that as various countries move up the income-per-head scale, more copper per head will be consumed—although not so much, perhaps, as would be consumed if substitution were not taking place. (Chapter 2 contains some information on consumption per head in various countries.) Moreover, the difference in consumption between the richest and the poorest of the industrial and semi-industrial countries is so great that an absolute downturn in the amount of copper being consumed is very difficult to contemplate.

Still, there are a number of very interesting arguments being devised which claim that there is something wrong with present consumption patterns in the industrial countries. As far as I can tell, these arguments have not realized any great popularity. As with many other controversial topics of our time, the main difficulty seems to be the deportment, appearance, and most of all the suspected motives of those individuals who are most vigorously pursuing the matter. At the same time it seems undeniable that a case having a mass appeal could be made for alternative patterns of consumption involving fewer items of the traditional type, and more sport, culture, and the like. Unfortunately, I doubt whether this will happen in the near future, but if it did I hardly think it would work to increase the demand for the products of the nonferrous metals industries.

The last point to be made in this section concerns the absence of short-run substitution activity the emphasis that this absence is fully consistent with received price theory. It seems clear that once the designs for various types of machinery have been accepted and production facilities established for the manufacture of this machinery, and once buyers and sellers are familiar with such things as thermal properties, conductivities, and so on, there is a great deal of reluctance—even on what appears to be legitimate cost reasons—to consider alternatives unles faced with very unfavorable price movements.

Another aspect of this problem can be considered by examining the following information taken from the transport equipment sector of the U.S. input-output table for 1947:

Input	Input Requirement per $10,000 Gross Output of Equipment
Transport Equipment	2,129
Iron and Steel	1,389
Machinery	1,069
Nonferrous Metals	210
Transportation	170
Textiles	150
Services	147
Chemicals	92
Electrical Power	33
Other Inputs	391
	—
Value Added	3,901

Copper and its substitutes fall within the nonferrous metals category, or within the classification of nonmetallic mineral products. Together these come to about 3 percent of the total value of a representative unit of transport equipment. Under the circumstances, a small increase or decrease in the price of copper would mean little for cost and profit figures in this industry. In any event, it would not call for the immediate replacement of costly machinery and other facilities for processing copper; and most important, since only a small part of the total value of a unit of this equipment is represented by copper, an increase in copper price could probably be passed on to final consumers.

OTHER PLANS FOR ORGANIZING

We have already touched on some aspects of controlling the price of copper. In Chapter 1 the results of some cartel forming was examined, and there was a short discussion of a valorization experiment by a group of producers only a few years ago. All these experiences left a great deal to be desired insofar as proving the effectiveness of such measures. For the most part they were bungled; and only in a few isolated instances did any sort of outcome result that could be said to reflect credit on the judgment of those involved.

Of late, however, other more sophisticated devices are being mooted about in the corridors of the elaborate conference halls where various committees and self-styled experts are gathered to look into these matters. Variants of the production control schemes of yesterday are still in the air, but this time they come embellished by plans for cartels in which votes will be cast by international organizations and consumer representatives as well as producer representatives. Price and quota agreements are to be resorted to; and in the event of losses sustained because of the development or the perfection of substitutes, a compensation fund is to be established that will subsidize those producers hardest hit. Obviously, the effective functioning of an organ of this nature is almost inconceivable, and most of the discussion taking this approach can be classified as sheer fantasy. The only justification for this discussion continuing, in fact, is that many of the proponents of such an organization hope to obtain well-paying non-jobs within its secretariat.

A more satisfactory program has been offered by Peter Bohm [1968] in his study dealing with the pricing of copper. He would like some of the more competent international organizations interested in stable copper prices (such as the International Monetary Fund) to form a sort of credit institute which, during periods of rising prices, would funnel loans from copper producers to copper buyers, going in the opposite direction when prices are falling. In principle I agree with some of this, although it seems to me that periods of rising prices are periods in which productive investments outside the copper industry should be made. However, since most of these countries have only a limited capacity to absorb investments during a given time span, loans to copper consumers or to consuming countries could be looked upon as a way of smoothing out the stream of investments that constitute the development process. This is so since producer countries would be receiving interest and amortization, and also borrowing themselves, when prices were low. Equally important, once this sort of arrangement is institutionalized, it might help to dampen, in the producer countries, some of the luxury consumption that seems to go with a booming market.

One of the measures under the longest consideration has been the establishment of a buffer stock. The popularity of this device for controlling the price of copper has resulted, I feel sure, from a misinterpretation of the effectiveness of the tin buffer stock. Many investigators have unfortunately come to the conclusion that the return of the tin price to acceptable levels was due to the buffer stock assisted by some export controls, when actually it was the other way around. The trend was brought under control by export restrictions, while the buffer stock ironed out some of the less extreme fluctuations.[4]

As late as January 1973, the price of tin had fallen to such a level

[4]For more on this, see Banks [1972].

that export controls had to be tightened. The amount of tin that could be exported was determined for each country on the basis of their quarterly exports of the previous year. The role assigned the tin buffer stock was to sell tin in case the price started to rise too fast.

It should be emphasized that there is no reason in *principle* why a buffer stock for copper should not succeed merely because the tin buffer stock has not been a roaring success. The United States maintains a strategic stockpile that has occasionally contained more than a million tons of copper, and it is clear that the U.S. domestic price was controlled to some extent by this stockpile during the period of 1965–68. One of the things that we observe in this case, however, is that the stockpile was being used to control a rising price, which means that it was selling relatively inexpensive copper at premium prices.

In considering the actions of the U.S. stockpile authorities between 1964 and 1970, it would be a mistake to take these actions out of context with the many other policies designed to influence the copper industry, as well as various other raw materials industries. To my way of thinking these policies were a sad comment on the mentality of the federal bureaucracy during those years, and even more so on their superiors in the legislative and executive branches of the government. By concentrating on price rather than capacity, such agencies as the Office of Emergency Planning (OEP), General Services Administration (GSA), Department of Commerce, and a few others must share no small part of the blame for one of the most insidious inflations in American history. In addition they were instrumental in delivering U.S. consumers into the tender, good graces of foreign producers. Although in general I am an optimist, I do not believe that this romance will have a happy ending.

The Japanese government has recently let it be known that it is prepared to take a more active part in the establishment and management of a buffer stock. Since 1970, a Japanese Metal Center has existed in London, and a kind of Japanese stabilization plan for copper has been drawn up. The overall intention is to counter speculative movements on the copper market by selling copper when the price is high and buying when the price is low. Some copper would also be held, and with the Metal Center acting as an information collector and dispenser, hedging operations by Japanese firms would be greatly facilitated. Also mentioned is the possibility that this hedging would be able to smooth out some of the smaller fluctuations.

Up to now the resources at the disposal of the Metal Center and similar groups (such as the Copper Stabilization Organization, and relevant departments within the University for the Development of Mineral Resources) have been limited; but if the Japanese government could, in fact, contemplate the establishment of a buffer stock of about a third or a half the size of the United States strategic stock pile, they could probably keep the price of copper at any level they choose—at least for a while. Just what size buffer stock the Japanese have in mind is difficult to find out. I have heard figures of up to 350,000 tons, although I have not heard just how an inventory of this size could be financed. (At present copper prices, 50,000 tons would be expensive to finance.) However, the Japanese will soon be using 1 million tons of copper a year, and as a result they may be prepared to make a rather large investment in price stability.

Finally, it should be noted that the Intergovernmental Council of Copper Exporting Countries (CIPEC) will be working to influence copper prices via export and production control, and negotiation with the main consuming countries. The problem here, as I see it, is that the CIPEC countries are at such a different level of economic development, and have economic and social systems of such disparity, that a synchronized price and capacity policy is going to be difficult to work out—difficult but not impossible, as the OPEC countries have shown with oil.

Chapter Seven

Consumption and Price: Introduction to an Econometric Analysis

On the basis of evidence submitted by most econometricians who have worked with commodity models, it seems unlikely that we are going to see, in the near future, econometric models of the commodity markets that approach the sophistication of macro-econometric models. There are several reasons for this. The first, quite obviously, is the absence of data-collecting facilities for commodities comparable to those available for aggregate economic variables such as income, consumption, etc. In conjunction with this there is a shortage of variables, which means that data-collecting facilities should, in addition to such things as price and output, be obtaining information on costs, capacity, and other variables of a microeconomic nature: variables having to do with the installations where these commodities are produced. This is asking a great deal. Finally, there is a poverty of forms into which the basic supply-demand relationships can be worked.

For these reasons, when it comes to things like price predictions for most raw materials, econometrics acting alone is not so much the wave of the future as the wave of the past. At the same time econometrics used together with economic theory, economic history, and an institutional study of the relevant market is an indispensible device for understanding the mechanics of a commodity market. From such an understanding, price forecasts may indeed be possible.

My original intention was to extend the analysis presented below into a very large and fairly complex econometric model; however, since Fisher, Cootner, and Baily [1972] have just constructed such a model, it would be an arrogant waste of time (and energy) for me to use valuable space in an attempt to duplicate their results.[1] Instead I would like to carry on an elementary discussion of some of the issues involved in formulating this kind of model.

---

[1] The best elementary treatment of the topics discussed in this and the following chapter is Wallis [1972]. Chapter 3 is especially important for its discussion of adaptive expectations and partial adjustment.

101

DYNAMIC EQUATION

The type of equation that is of immediate interest is called a dynamic equation, and it appears on the basis of existing research that this type of equation is of great importance in explaining the demand for both durable goods and inter- mediate inputs. Behind this type of equation is the assumption that purchases either cannot or will not be brought to a certain level in "zero time," in response to, for example, a change in price. In the present example this type of adjust- ment behavior seems relevant, since the purchases (C_t) being discussed here are for both current inputs and inventories. Thus even though the buying of inputs to be used for current production may conceivably react instantaneously to stimuli of one type or another, adjustments in the level of inventories almost certainly takes time, and this by itself should cause C_t to exhibit the postulated behavior. A diagrammatic presentation of this concept is given in Figure 7–1.

In Figure 7–1 the original price is P_o, and the long-run demand curve is D_o. If demand adjusted immediately to a fall in price to P^*, we would move to C_t^*. Instead, in the very short run, with price P^*, demand increases only to C_1; but over time we get an asymptotic movement to C_t^*. Another typical inter- mediate demand curve is D_2, and C_2 is an intermediate consumption. The reader

Figure 7–1. Demand Adjustment Following Changes in Price *(P)* or Change in an Aggregate Variable *(X)*

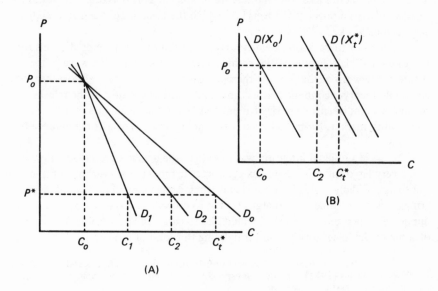

can draw as many of these intermediate demand curves as he wishes, either to the left or to the right of D_2.

It is a simple matter to show that the law of adjustment for this model is $C_t = C_{t-1} + \lambda(C_t^* - C_{t-1})$, where C_t^* is the equilibrium value of demand, and where when $C_t = C_t^*$, we have no further change in the variable.[2] If, as in Figure 3–1, we relate demand to price by $C_t^* = \alpha + \theta P_t$, and put this expression into the adjustment equation, we get:

$$C_t = \lambda\alpha + (1 - \lambda)C_{t-1} + \lambda\theta P_t \qquad (1)$$

When $C_t = C_{t-1} = C_t$ we have an equilibrium (equal to unchanging consumption) and we are back on D_o. This is so since by substituting $C_t = C_{t-1} = C_t^*$ into (1) we get $C_t^* = \alpha + \theta P_t$.

It should be carefully observed here that P_t took values P_o and P^* in Figure 7–1. The change in P_t initiated changes in C_t, with the time path of C_t determined by the parameters of the system. In the figure we had an initial equilibrium at P_o and C_o, with $C_o = \alpha + \theta P_o$. With the change in P_o to P^*, C increased and converged asymptotically to C_t^*, and in the final equilibrium we had $C_t^* = \alpha + \theta P^*$. In both these equilibrium situations we are on D_o. The long-run demand curve thus denotes equilibrium positions.

It may happen that instead of an actual change in price we have an expected change, with demand altering in anticipation of the expected price. This would make the idea of a gradual change in C_t seem even more reasonable, since buyers are apt to be cautious until their forecasts concerning the new price are strengthened by experience. In this situation expectations must be "formed" on P_t: we must explain *how* we expect price to change and introduce this hypothesis for expected price directly into the analysis. (It should be remembered, however, that the reason for dealing with equilibrium or expected prices in the above discussion was purely illustrative. Instead of price we could have used an aggregate variable such as income or industrial production, in which case an expression such as $C_t^* = \alpha + \theta X_t$ would have been put into the adjustment

[2] In continuous form this is:

$$C = \lambda \int_o^t e^{-\lambda Z} C^*(T - Z)dZ$$

The lag is assumed to be of the Koyck type, with the weight in period Z being $\lambda e^{-\lambda Z}$. If we have a change in C in the form of a step function at time $T-Z$, with the new desired value of C being $\bar{C}$, we get:

$$C = \lambda \bar{C}^* \int_o^t e^{-\lambda Z}dZ = (1 - e^{-\lambda t})\bar{C}^*$$

What we have is an asymptotic movement to the new equilibrium $\bar{C}^*$.

equation. In Figure 3–1, for example, price is constant, but the value of X_t changes from X_O to X_t^*. Consumption then again moves asymptotically from C_O to C_t^*.)

In the beginning of the previous paragraph, adjustment has been mixed together with expectations. Usually these are kept apart, although, as the reader will later see, the adjustment model in (1) is equivalent to the "adaptive" expectations model. If we take for the first expectations model the case of "extrapolative" expectations, and we employ the conventional formulation, we get a model without dynamic effects, or "adjustment."

The algebraic expression for expected price using extrapolative expectations is $P_t^e = P_{t-1} + \phi \Delta P_{t-x}$, and with the simplest lag structure we have $P_t^e = P_{t-1} + \theta \Delta P_{t-1} = P_{t-1} + \phi (P_{t-1} - P_{t-2})$. If we have consumption as a function of expected price, or $C_t = \alpha + \theta P_t^e$, we get $C_t = \alpha + \theta P_{t-1} + \theta \phi \Delta P_{t-1}$. The estimating equation would be $C_t = \beta_o + \beta_1 P_{t-1} + \beta_2 \Delta P_{t-1}$, and so $\alpha = \beta_o$, $\theta = \beta_1$, and $\phi = \beta_2/\beta_1$.

At the same time I want to explore the possibility of using extrapolative expectations and getting a dynamic effect in a manner suggested by Witherell [1967]. What we have now is an initial equilibrium where actual price is equal to expected price. We then have a change in expected price, which instigates a change in consumption. There is no point in starting the analysis over, and so I will use $P_t^e = P_{t-1} + \phi \Delta P_{t-1}$ in equation (1), with $P_t = P_t^e$. We then get

$$C_t = \lambda \alpha + (1-\lambda)C_{t-1} + \lambda \theta P_{t-1} + \lambda \theta \phi \Delta P_{t-1} \qquad (2)$$

This can be estimated by employing

$$C_t = \beta_o + \beta_1 C_{t-1} + \beta_2 P_{t-1} + \beta_3 \Delta P_{t-1} \qquad (3)$$

From (2) and (3) we get $\lambda = 1 - \beta_1$, $\alpha = \beta_o/1 - \beta_1$, $\theta = \beta_2/1 - \beta_1$, and $\phi = \beta_3/\beta_2$. Thus, in this simplified case these four parameters can be solved out. As can be seen in the simple econometric work presented below, this specification was used on several occasions.

Before continuing, it might be worthwhile to look at the nature of the variable C_t. This is, of course, a flow variable: its units are tons per year, and the models being discussed here are flow adjustment models.[3] This is brought out since, as pointed out in appendix A, a strong case can be made for framing

---

[3]Meghnad Desai [1972] has pointed out that the variable C_t should be referred to as "disappearance," since in order to call it demand stocks would have to be treated explicitly. Since I agree in the discussion in this chapter (and in appendix A) that the key demand is the demand for stocks, I am in sympathy with this point of view. However, we know from the theory of stock-flow models that the flow demand is a demand that will be used for current input *plus* stock changes. Thus C_t is a flow demand, and I have used it in that sense.

the analysis in stock terms. The reader who has examined this appendix probably realizes that the algebraic delineation of such a model does not present overwhelming problems, but unfortunately econometric work in the commodity field has, as far as I know, never managed to produce an acceptable stock adjustment model. The reason for this seems to be that much of the data having to do with inventory movements is unsatisfactory; the behavioral relationships underlying such models are not as clear as once thought; and there are probably important nonlinearities involved that have vitiated the techniques of simple regression analysis. To get some idea of the complexity of supply-demand relationships in the industry, Figure 7–2 should be studied.

Inventory behavior is obviously very important in this market, and in attempting to sort out the various forces at work, a great deal of time was taken up with the well-known stock adjustment form of the accelerator equation:

$$I_t - I_{t-1} = \psi \, (I_t^* - I_{t-1}) \qquad\qquad (4)$$

Equilibrium inventory I_t^* was then assumed to be a function of an income type variable X_t, expected price, and so on. $I_t - I_{t-1}$ can then be defined as the investment in stocks, and is proportional to the difference between desired

Figure 7–2. U.S. Supply-Demand Relationships for Copper, 1966

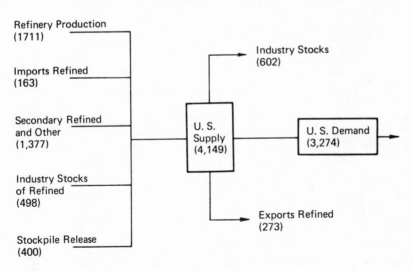

Source: U.S. Government Stockpile Reports.
Note: Units in thousands of short tons.

and actual stocks. With, for example, $I_t^* = \eta X_t$ we get $I_t = \psi \eta X_t + (1 - \psi)I_{t-1}$, where the integral of this expression is:

$$I_t = \psi \eta \sum_{t=0}^{\alpha} (1 - \psi)^i X_{t-i} \tag{5}$$

In considering the simplicity of this and similar equations, no difficulty was anticipated in estimating parameters such as ψ and η. However, as it turned out, this estimation was not solved.

Extrapolative expectations have not, to my knowledge, gained any wide circle of admirers among econometricians. Since we know very little about how expectations are formed in real life, the question might be raised as to why we prefer one method of formation to another. A partial answer is that extrapolative expectations introduces some rather serious biases into our estimating equation, and in addition they seem just a little too simple for our very complex world—there are other possibilities that are intuitively more satisfying.[4]

The other type of expectations hypothesis that will be examined here is the adaptive. This involves taking expected price as a weighted average of

[4]It is interesting to note that the Houthakker-Taylor model giving the demand for durable goods leads to an equation similar to (2) and (3). Employing the notation of this chapter, we have $C(t) = \alpha_0 + \alpha_1 I(t) + \alpha_2 X(t)$ in continuous form. To get rid of the inventory term we employ the expression $C_t = I_t - I_{t-1} + \delta I_{t-1}$, where δ is a depreciation rate, and in the context of the present discussion is equivalent to the rate at which the existing stock of the commodity is run down via its use as a current input in the production process. In continuous form we have:

$$C = \frac{dI}{dt} + \delta I \tag{6}$$

Then, differentiating $C = \alpha_0 + \alpha_1 I + \alpha_2 X$ gives:

$$\frac{dC}{dt} = \alpha_1 \frac{dI}{dt} + \alpha_2 \frac{dX}{dt} \tag{7}$$

If dI/dt from (6) is put in (7), and the result is added to $C = \alpha_0 + \alpha_1 I + \alpha_2 X$ multiplied by δ, we get:

$$\frac{dC}{dt} = \alpha_0 + (\alpha_1 - \delta)C + \alpha_2 \frac{dX}{dt} + \alpha_2 \delta X \tag{8}$$

Using a discrete approximation of the derivatives gives as the estimating equation for (8):

$$C_t = \beta_0 + \beta_1 C_{t-1} + \beta_2 \Delta X_t + \beta_3 X_{t-1}$$

For further aspects of this type of analysis see Houthakker and Taylor [1966].

past prices in a manner popularized by Koyck [1954].[5] In the development below the stochastic term will be introduced explicitly, since it is of interest to examine the composite error term in the estimating equation.

To begin with, we have $C_t = \alpha + \theta P_t^e + u_t$, where u_t is the stochastic term. Adaptive expectations then call for $P_t^e = P_{t-1}^e + \lambda(P_{t-1} - P_{t-1}^e)$. Putting P_t^e into C_t gives $C_t = \alpha + \theta \ [P_{t-1}^e + \lambda(P_{t-1} - P_{t-1}^e)] + u_t$. If $C_t = \alpha + \theta P_t^e + u_t$ is lagged one period, multiplied by $(1 - \lambda)$, and subtracted from the previous C_t, we get as our structural equation

$$C_t = \alpha\lambda + (1 - \lambda)C_{t-1} + \theta\lambda P_{t-1} + [u_t - (1 - \lambda)u_{t-1}].$$

If we now look only at the nonstochastic part of this equation we see that it differs from the adjustment equation (1) by containing P_{t-1} instead of P_t. This situation can be rectified by changing the timing of expectations: instead of the formulation used above take $P_t^e = P_{t-1}^e + \lambda(P_t - P_{t-1}^e)$. Manipulating this as in the above paragraph gives (1) exactly. In choosing between these two versions, the latter probably makes more sense when considering production rather than consumption, since the issue with production is a long-run normal or expected price rather than a simple forecast. For this reason it will introduce the discussion in the next chapter.

The estimating equation is $C_t = \beta_o + \beta_1 C_{t-1} + \beta_2 P_{t-1} + [u_t - (1 - \lambda)u_{t-1}]$. This is close enough to (3) for the reader to apply the discussion following that equation, but some problem remains because of the stochastic term. As the reader probably remembers, one of the criteria placed on the stochastic term when ordinary least squares is to be used is no serial correlation: $E(\epsilon_t, \epsilon_{t-1}) = 0$, where this expression represents an off-diagonal term in the variance-covariance matrix. In the present case $E(\epsilon_t, \epsilon_{t-1}) = E\{[u_t - (1 - \lambda)u_{t-1}] \ [u_{t-1} - (1 - \lambda)u_{t-2}]\}$. Here it is clear that if we assume no serial correlation among individual disturbances we have $E(u_t u_{t-1})$, $E(u_t, u_{t-2})$, and $E(u_{t-1} u_{t-2})$ equal to zero; but $E[-(1 - \lambda)u_{t-1} u_{t-1}] = -(1 - \lambda)$ Var u_{t-1}, and since Var u_{t-1} is nonzero, the composite stochastic term displays serial correlation. This, of course, means that the use of ordinary least squares would result in estimates of α, θ, and λ that would not be consistent.[6]

A few of the more satisfactory of the many experiments I ran are shown in Table 7–1. These results are inserted for two reasons. First, for completeness, since although they are not bias free, Takeuchi [1972][7] has indicated

---

[5] An equally important reference is Nerlove [1958].

[6] Other estimating problems are caused by the presence of the lagged dependent variable, and the compounded biases could be very serious indeed if ordinary least squares were used.

[7] It should be pointed out that the equations discussed by Takenchi are not the same equations as presented here.

that they can be used for some rough projection work, and also because one of the objects of these experiments was to confirm the presence (or absence) of various expectational structures.

In Tables 7–1 and 7–2 and in the next section, the following notation will be observed:

P_t: The London Metal Exchange price of refined copper, deflated by the wholesale price index in the relevant country, 1963 = 100

P_{ut}: The U.S. price of refined copper, deflated by the U.S. general wholesale price index

P'_{ut}: The undeflated U.S. price of refined copper in cents per pound

I_t: Inventories of refined copper in thousands of metric tons

C'_t: The total consumption of refined copper (primary and secondary) in period t, in thousands of metric tons

C_t: The consumption of primary refined copper in period t, in thousands of metric tons

X_t: The index of industrial production for the relevant country, 1963 = 100

ΔG: Change in the U.S. Federal Reserve Board's index of inventories of durable goods

D_i: A dummy variable

e: Elasticity with regard to price *(P)* or the index of industrial production *(X)*. Subscripts s and L signify short and long run.

The logic behind the deflation of the price by the wholesale price index is simple, and, among others, Herfindahl [1959] has explained it in great detail. In brief, what this deflation does is to relate the cost of copper as an input to the price of the output in which it is used, and it also says something about its desirability relative to other inputs. Thus, if the price of the output, the input in question, and relative substitutes for the input were to double, we would expect no decline in the demand for the input per unit of output.

The basic data consisted of yearly observations covering the period of 1953–68. A number of experiments employing quarterly data were also run, but these were not particularly satisfactory, and in addition it was thought that using yearly instead of quarterly data helps to reduce the distributed lag bias since there was less correlation between present and lagged values. When a dummy variable was used its value was unity for the years indicated, and zero otherwise. *"t"* ratios are in parenthesis, and when applicable the Durbin-Watson (D.W.) statistic is shown.

Table 7–1. Regression Estimates for Primary Refined Copper, Major Consumers (C_t)

	U.S.	U.K.	France	Germany	Italy	Japan
Constant Term	1030.50	309.16	57.99	463.36	67.5	0.511
C_{t-1}		0.315 (1.288)	0.400 (2.19)	0.324 (2.06)		
P_t			−0.310 (2.53)	−0.761 (2.893)		
P_{t-1}		−0.987 (2.24)			−0.299 (4.01)	
P_{ut-1}	−2.942 (2.44)					
X_t			1.10 (3.04)	2.802 (3.334)		
X_{t-1}	6.318 (6.27)	3.145 (2.310)			0.519 (6.14)	
Y (Income)						1.0264 (14.50)
ΔC_t	72.290 (8.61)					
ΔX_t				7.075 (3.357)		
D	139 (3.19)	−40.216 (1.106)				
$\bar{R}^2$	0.9482	0.6400	0.9250	0.9284	0.712	0.940
$D.W.$	2.161		1.540		1.600	1.340
e_P	−0.294				−0.390	
e_{PS}		−0.252	−0.253	−0.221		
e_{PL}		−0.368	−0.421	−0.328		
e_i	0.407				0.524	1.026
e_{iS}		0.570	0.540	0.530		
e_{iL}		0.830	0.900	0.790		

Notes:
1. Dummy years, U.S.: 1953; U.K. 1956–58.
2. Equation for Japan: $\text{Log } C = a + b \text{ Log } Y$; estimated using ordinary least squares.
3. Methods of estimation: ordinary least squares and maximum liklihood.

Some comments on these results are in order. The elasticity with respect to industrial production for the U.S. equations is undoubtedly too low. One of the difficulties here is that with the U.S. as both a major producer and consumer of copper, simultaneous equation bias is present. After formulating and estimating a simultaneous equation model and getting unsatisfactory results,

Table 7–2.   Regression Estimates for Primary plus Secondary Refined Copper, (C'_t)

	U.S.	U.K.	France	Germany
Constant term	1057.0	268.90	59.67	591.0
C'_{t-1}		0.367 (1.675)	0.274 (1.380)	0.442 (2.776)
P_t			−0.2790 (2.12)	−0.55435 (2.080)
P_{t-1}		−0.8479 (2.13)		
P_{ut-1}	−3.408 (3.160)			
X_t		2.880 (2.24)	2.034 (3.58)	2.800 (2.665)
X_{t-1}	6.410 (7.10)			
ΔG_t	75.899 (9.67)			
ΔX_t				8.316 (3.455)
D	127 (3.18)			
$\bar{R}^2$	0.9579	0.615	0.960	0.9458
$D.W.$	2.129			
e_P	−0.294			
e_{PS}		−0.177	−0.152	−0.127
e_{PL}		−0.290	−0.210	−0.228
e_i	0.407			
e_{iS}		0.417	0.657	0.428
e_{iL}		0.660	0.910	0.752

Notes:
1. Dummy variable for U.S.: 1953.
2. Methods of estimation: ordinary least squares and maximum liklihood.

I have done some experimenting with quarterly data and formulations that were much more disaggregated. My results are as yet tentative, but they indicate elasticities in the 0.8 − 1.00 range.

In the case of Japan the trend obviously overwhelmed all other influences. The situation here, in many respects, seemed to parallel that of Germany, where price elasticities seem to be quite low, and where in many experiments the regressions gave positive elasticities. The explanation seems to be that both

Germany and Japan are important consumers of copper, and this consumption is growing very fast. The purchase of copper involves shifts in the demand curve faster than corresponding shifts can take place in supply and, in addition, encourages buying to counter expected price increases.

The effect of all this was to make it impossible to isolate price effects through conventional econometric techniques. In fact on examination of the various correlation and partial correlation coefficients, I came to the conclusion that in many cases *negative* price elasticities must be regarded with a certain suspicion.[8]

PRICE AND INVENTORIES

The approach to price was through the relationship between desired and actual inventories. Inventory holders have some idea of the ratio of inventories to consumption that they wish to maintain. When this ratio rises they decrease price (attempting to increase sales), and they do the opposite when it falls.

The definition for stock changes is $\Delta I = S_t - D_t$, where D_t is the demand for current inputs. The variable that has been used up to now is C_t (which covers current inputs *and* stock changes), and this will continue to be the case. While D_t would probably be more satisfactory from the theoretical point of view, there were some problems in obtaining it for more than a few years. The formulation that seemed most reasonable for the purposes of this chapter was:

$$\Delta P = b_1 \ (k_1 \ \Delta C - \Delta I)$$

When $k_1 \ \Delta C = \Delta I$, the desired change in inventories was equal to the actual, and the price is stationary. A variant of this equation is $\Delta P = b_2 \ (k_2 \ C - I)$, and here when desired inventories $(k_2 C)$ equals actual inventories (I), ΔP is zero.

In neither of these cases did my econometric work prove satisfactory. As far as I could tell, the principal problem was the collinearity between C and I.

---

[8] As an example of what is being discussed here it might be of interest to postulate demand as a function of present price *and* future (expected) price. We can then write:

$$q_t = q_t \ (p_t, p^e_{t+1}) = b_0 + b_1 p_t + b_2 p^e_{t+1} \qquad b_1 < 0, b_2 > 0$$

Taking expected price as $p^e_{t+1} = p_t + \lambda(p_t - p_{t-1})$, which means using extrapolative expectations, we get:

$$q_t = b_0 + [b_1 + b_2 (1 + \lambda)] p_t - b_2 \lambda p_{t-1} \qquad \lambda \gtreqless 0$$

We see that we can have $[b_1 + b_2 (1 + \lambda)] \gtreqless 0$, depending on the size of b_1, b_2, and λ. Thus if we were attempting to fit a demand curve, speculative effects could conceivably give a positive relationship between q_t and p_t, instead of the expected negative.

The use of the ratio C/I thus follows logically and, in addition to helping reduce collinearity, provides a formulation that helps to reduce the simultaneity bias—assuming that to be relevant here. Employing quarterly data for the period of 1960–65, when the U.S. copper industry appeared to be in a normal situation with steady expansion and no strikes, two equations were estimated. In addition to the notation given earlier, Q is production of refined copper, I' producers' inventories, and I'' consumers' inventories. "t" ratios are in parenthesis and the Durbin-Watson (D.W.) statistic is given.

$$P_{ut} = 27.17 + 0.602 \left(\frac{Q_t}{I'_{t-1}} \right) \qquad \bar{R}^2 = 0.775 \qquad \text{D.W.} = 1.76$$
$$(2.11)$$

$$P_{ut} = 17.54 + 0.305 \left(\frac{C_{t-1}}{I''_{t-1}} \right) + 0.0276 \, Q_t \qquad \bar{R}^2 = 0.664 \qquad \text{D.W.} = 1.76$$
$$\quad\quad (3.00) \qquad\qquad (3.01)$$

As given here the only thing these equations can do is to provide a weak confirmation of the basic form of the relationship. The expression C/I or Q/I should have been inverted, and even then a lower limit would have been put on the price. What is needed is an equation of the form

$$P = \alpha + \beta \frac{\Delta I}{\Delta C}$$

or something similar in which, for example, $\Delta I / \Delta C$ can be negative as well as positive. Fisher, Cootner, and Baily have such an equation, and the interested reader should refer to it.

The final comment in this chapter also refers to inventories. One way of approaching this problem is to postulate that desired inventories of most non-ferrous metals are based not only on current consumption but also on price expectations. One could, in fact, distinguish between a "transaction" and a "speculative" motive for inventory holding.

To understand this better, consider a situation where flow consumption and production are in equilibrium, and actual stocks are equal to desired stocks. At this point assume an exogenous increase in demand that increases price, while at the same time assuming that price expectations are unchanged. It is then possible to identify a force calling for a reduction in inventories, since the gap between expected and actual price is reduced, and thus the present level of inventory holding is too high. In other words, a part of this new demand should be supplied from inventories, thus taking the "profit" that is the difference between the price at which releases from inventory can be sold, and the price at which these stocks were bought plus storage. At the same time there is another force calling for inventories to be increased, since an increased current demand calls for inventories to be adjusted upwards in response to the "transactions" motive.

Determining just how this type of behavior fixes the time paths of price, production, and inventories will be left to the reader who has a talent for solving very complicated systems of difference or differential equations. Similarly, doing econometric work on such a system would undoubtedly require nonlinear techniques that are at present only of limited use—even to those fortunate enough to comprehend them.

In Figure 7–3 a simple model containing some of the elements of the previous discussion is drawn. In the figure *S* is supply, *C* consumption, *P* price, *AI* actual inventories, *DI* desired inventories, *EP* expected price, and *EV* exogenous variables.

Figure 7–3. Simple Supply-Demand System Showing Interaction of Actual and Desired Inventories

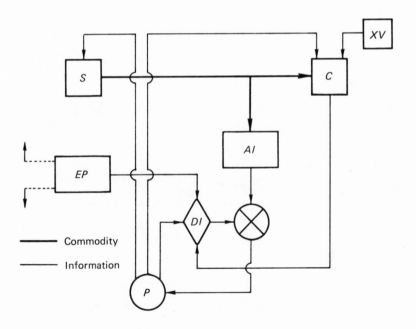

Chapter Eight

Some Econometric Aspects
of the Supply of Copper

The discussion here will follow the same logic used in the previous chapter. In the present case, however, the relation between supply and price is clearer than that between consumption and price, since (with costs given) it would be difficult to imagine supply as a function of any other variable.

Once again we have our choice of two conceptual models, the "adjustment" and the "expectational." As it happens, regression methods cannot distinguish between the two; the choice must be strictly a priori. In order to assist in making this decision it should be observed that both these models, beginning with $S_t = \alpha\lambda + (1-\lambda)S_{t-1} + \lambda\theta P_t$, can be reduced to a weighted average of present and former prices.[1] The simplest way to see this is to lag the equation for S_t and use it to replace S_{t-1} in the same equation. The result is $S_t = \alpha\lambda + (1-\lambda)[\alpha\lambda + (1-\lambda)S_{t-2} + \lambda\theta P_{t-2}] + \lambda\theta P_{t-1}$. Repeated application of this procedure gives:

$$S_t = \alpha + \lambda\theta \sum_{i=o}^{\infty} (1-\lambda)^i P_{t-i}$$

Still, on logical grounds, the adjustment model appears to be more appropriate in the present context. Changes in production do take time; and it seems reasonable that firms would prefer to regard the *present* price as an indicator of future or equilibrium price, rather than some weighted average of prices. (In this way, in fact, it is possible to introduce the expression "naive" expectations, where expected price = present price).

The following exposition thus assumes the adjustment hypothesis.

[1] As shown in the previous chapter, the adjustment equation and the version of the adaptive hypothesis that has $P_t^e = P_{t-1} + \lambda(P_t - P_{t-1}^e)$, will both give $S_t = \alpha\lambda + (1-\lambda)S_{t-1} + \lambda\theta P_t$. In general, in this chapter, 'S' simply replaces the 'C' used in Chapter 7.

As shown in the figure, following a change in price from P_0 to P_1, short-run supply is S' and over time there is an asymptotic movement to S_1. An intermediate supply curve is S_i, with supply S'', and price still constant at P_1. The adjustment equation is obviously $S_t = S_{t-1} + \lambda (S_1 - S_{t-1})$, which can be proved by writing this expression as a difference equation, $S_t - (1 - \lambda)S_{t-1} = \lambda S_1$, and solving. This gives $S_t = (S_0 - S_1)(1 - \lambda)^t + S_1$, and with $0 < \lambda < 1$, which is the usual constraint for λ, we have an asymptotic movement of supply to S_1 where $S_{t-1} = S_t = S_1$. If we now relate S_1 to price by a linear relation of the type $S_1 = \alpha + \theta P_t$, and use this in the adjustment equation, we get as before

$$S_t = \lambda \alpha + (1 - \lambda)S_{t-1} + \lambda \theta P_t \tag{1}$$

This expression will now be presented employing a device of the type associated with multiplier analysis. This is shown in (A) of Figure 8–2. Note that the production equilibrium is $S_{t-1} = S_t = S_0$; while the slope of ZZ', which is the coefficient of S_{t-1}, is $(1 - \lambda)$; and the intercept of ZZ' is a function of P_t (which means that in the initial equilibrium the intercept is a function of P_0). The initial equilibrium is also shown in (B) of Figure 8–2.
Corresponding to Figure 7–1 we now have Figure 8–1, where with a price change from P_0 to P_1, supply begins to increase but does not go at once to its new equilibrium value S_1.

Figure 8–1. Changes in Supply Given an Increase in Price from P_0 to P_1

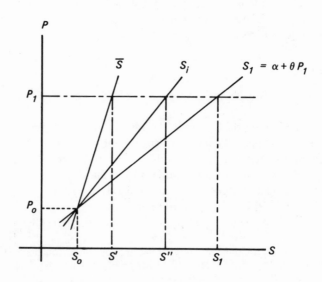

Figure 8-2. The Initial Equilibrium in a Dynamic Supply Model

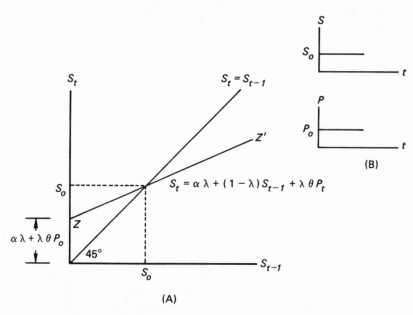

(A)

(B)

If we now have an increase in price to P_1 (due, for example, to an increase in demand), ZZ' shifts up. The new equilibrium is S_1, but as postulated above, this cannot be reached instantaneously. In the first period the increase in production is TT', while in the second it is $T'A$, and so on. We thus have a multiplier sequence consisting of:

$$\lambda\theta\,(P_1-P_o)\left[1+(1-\lambda)+(1-\lambda)^2+\dots\right]=\frac{\lambda\theta(P_1-P_o)}{1-(1-\lambda)}=\theta(P_1-P_o) \tag{2}$$

This expression serves to show that $\lambda\theta\,(P_1-P_o)$ is equal to TT', while $\lambda(1-\lambda)\theta(P_1-P_o)$ is equal to $T'A$, and so on. It is also interesting to note that if producers were willing to supply the increase in demand $\Delta S = S_1-S_o$ by drawing down inventories, as well as from current production, the amount drawn down would be $T'T''$ in the first period, $T'T''-T'A$ in the second period, and so forth—assuming the full amount ΔS would be supplied in each period. Otherwise inventory releases would be some fraction of amounts as $T'T''$. These inventory releases can also be summed in a series of the type shown in (2). The diagrammatic representation of the discussion in this paragraph is in (A) of Figure 8-3, while a simpler version of what is taking place (shown in continuous form for simplicity) is in (B) of the Figure.

Figure 8–3. Movement to the Final Equilibrium in a Dynamic Supply Model

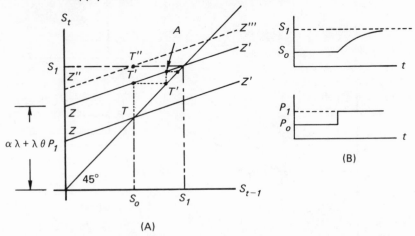

(A)

(B)

An argument might also be advanced that production could in fact be increased by $T'T''$ (to S_1) in the first period if consumers were willing to pay a price corresponding to the intercept Z''. (The reasoning here, quite simply, is that every value of the intercept corresponds to a price. The initial intercept corresponded to P_o, the increased intercept due to the shift upward of ZZ' corresponds to P_1, and so on. The same thing could be said about increases in production in the first period. An increase in production of TT' corresponded to a price of P_1. There must, therefore, be a price that will obtain a *total* production increase of TT'' in the first period.) As shown above $\lambda \theta (P_1 - P_o) = TT'$, and so $\lambda \theta (P_x - P_o) = TT'' = \Delta S$. P_x is the price corresponding to intercept Z'', and if the essentially linear assumptions that are being used here continue to hold, it is equal to $P_x = P_o + \Delta S/\lambda \theta$. Alternatively it might be postulated that this is the price that is necessary for producers to provide consumers with the increase ΔS by producing TT', and taking $T'T''$ from stocks.

THE ESTIMATING EQUATION

The estimating equation corresponding to (1) is $S_t = \beta_o + \beta_1 S_{t-1} + \beta_2 P_t + u_t$, where u_t is the error term. We thus see that $\lambda = 1 - \beta_1$, $\alpha = \beta_o/1 - \beta_1$, and $\theta = \beta_2/1 - \beta_1$. If the lagging procedure used in the first section is resorted to with the estimating equation we get a composite error term $v_t = u_t + \beta_1 u_{t-1} + \beta_1^2 u_{t-2} + \ldots$, but this can be lagged, multiplied by β_1, and subtracted from v_t to give $u_t = v_t - \beta_1 v_{t-1}$. Once again we see that we have serially correlated error terms that the estimating method must take into account.

After a large number of experiments, the logarithmic form of the estimating equation was finally chosen. This simplifies the matter of obtaining elasticities, of course, since if we have $\text{Log } S_t = \beta_o + \beta_1 \text{ Log } S_{t-1} + \beta_2 \text{ Log } P_t$

we get as the short-run elasticity $e_{PS} = \beta_2$, and for the long-run elasticity (when $\text{Log } S_t = \text{Log } S_{t-1}$) we have $e_{PL} = \beta_2 / 1 - \beta_1$.

The supply being considered here is the supply of newly mined copper in thousands of metric tons (copper content), expressed as an index with 1963 the base year. P_t is the price of refined copper on the London Metal Exchange, while P_{ut} is the American copper price computed as an average of several prices, with these prices also in index form. D is a dummy which is unity for the years given, and zero otherwise. "t" ratios are in parenthesis. Where choosing an estimating method was concerned, some experiments were also made. All equations were estimated by ordinary least squares and a maximum liklihood technique. The results were compared, and what seemed to be the best equation was chosen. The basic data consisted of annual observations over the period of 1948–67.

Canada

$\text{Log } S_t = 0.21511 + 0.7949 \text{ Log } S_{t-1} + 0.2365 \text{ Log } P_{ut}$
$\qquad\qquad\qquad\quad (6.876)\qquad\qquad (2.245)$

$\bar{R}^2 = 0.8114 \quad e_{PS} = 0.2365 \qquad e_{PL} = 1.16$

Chile

$\text{Log } S_t = 0.1236 + 0.7694 \text{ Log } S_{t-1} + 0.2890 \text{ Log } P_{t-1}$
$\qquad\qquad\qquad (8.412)\qquad\qquad (2.670)$

$\bar{R}^2 = 0.920 \quad e_{PS} = 0.2890 \qquad e_{PL} = 1.22$

Zaire (Congo)

$\text{Log } S_t = 0.4144 + 0.7204 \text{ Log } S_{t-1} + 0.1726 \text{ Log } P_t + 0.031 \ D$
$\qquad\qquad\qquad\ (8.854)\qquad\qquad (3.12)\qquad\qquad (2.869)$

$\bar{R}^2 = 0.947 \quad e_{PS} = 0.1726 \qquad e_{PL} = 0.625 \qquad D: 1959–62$

Peru

$\text{Log } S_t = -0.2896 + 0.7240 \text{ Log } S_{t-1} + 0.542 \text{ Log } P_{t-1} + 0.210 \ D_s$
$\qquad\qquad\qquad\quad (7.00)\qquad\qquad (1.851)\qquad\qquad (2.750)$

$\bar{R}^2 = 0.947 \quad e_{PS} = 0.542 \qquad e_{PL} = 1.930 \qquad D_S: 1961–64$

U.S.A.

$\text{Log } S_t = 0.971 + 0.5190 \text{ Log } S_{t-1} + 0.310 \text{ Log } P_t - 0.027 \ D_a$
$\qquad\qquad\qquad (3.40)\qquad\qquad (2.17)\qquad\qquad (1.00)$

$\bar{R}^2 = 0.6501 \quad e_{PS} = 0.310 \qquad e_{PL} = 0.630 \qquad D_a: 1959–62$

Zambia: All experiments unsatisfactory

The short-run elasticities given above agree with those calculated by Newhouse and Sloan [1966] (as quoted by Takeuchi) employing ordinary and three pass least squares. Their data period, however, began and ended much earlier than the one employed here.

Attempts were also made to get supply equations for refined copper. Most of these experiments were unsuccessful, regardless of whether annual, bi-annual, or quarterly data was used, and regardless of the method of estimation.

The reader has also probably noticed that there are no time trend variables in the econometric work. The reason for this is simply because the use of such variables introduced an intolerable amount of multicollinearity into the analysis. Still, it can be seen from an examination of the data that there is a secular expansion of production which clearly ignores price. For example, Congolese production in 1960 was 66 percent higher than in 1951–52, although the deflated price of copper was about the same. In Zambia the same comparison gave a 120 percent difference, in Chile 42 percent, and in Peru 450 percent. In addition, the price in 1960 seemed to be on a plateau that was formed early in 1959 and lasted until about 1962, which meant that producers had plenty of time to make and carry through decisions to reduce production. A number of reasons could probably be cited as to why they chose not to, but the following are apparently the most important.

1. The marginal costs of production have generally been low relative to copper prices in the post-war periods. In fact, were it not for several rather peculiar structural aspects of the industry, production probably would have been been higher.

2. It is almost as expensive to reopen a shut-down mine as to sink a new one.

3. The system of contracting to sell the next year's output before it is produced, and at an unknown price, leaves producers without the incentive to alter production in response to price changes. Instead the tendency is to hold a uniform rate of capacity utilization of about 92 percent as long as normal profits are being made.

THE RATE OF GROWTH

The trend rate of growth of copper mining capacity seems to be slightly under 6 percent in the less developed countries, and about 4½ percent in the United States and Canada. It also appears that the rate of growth of industrial production in the major consuming countries is about 5½ percent, where this is a weighted average. If we take as a "safe" demand elasticity of copper with respect to industrial production a value of 0.75, we get for the growth of copper demand $n_I g = 0.75 \times 5.5 = 4.13$ percent. (On the other hand, taking a value of 0.90 as the elasticity will give a rate of growth of copper demand of 4.95 percent.) Under the circumstances, a downward thrust on prices is to be expected.

At the moment of writing, the price of copper is just once more beginning to recede from near record levels. These abnormally high prices can be explained by the recent strike in Chile. But a year ago, with the war in Vietnam coming to an end, more or less normal economic conditions prevailing in the major consuming countries, the price seemed to have stabilized at about 50–53 cents per pound; and it certainly seemed to be the case that had the building out of capacity continued as scheduled in Chile, the price of copper would have fallen below 50 cents.

At least two factors seem to me to be of crucial importance when trying to judge just where the copper price is liable to go. The first is technology. The newest installations will probably be able to continue production with prices well under 50 cents. The Bougainville operation referred to earlier will continue to produce with prices as low as 30 cents. Moreover, I cannot imagine, for political and other reasons, production stopping in the less developed countries as long as variable costs are covered (and perhaps not even then). Just what these costs are at the present time is difficult to say, since wages have increased considerably of late, but a figure of 30–35 cents would have been reasonable for the CIPEC countries just a few years ago.

In addition, the limit on the increase in capacity in the less developed countries is to a great extent a political matter. Given the role that copper plays in the export income of these countries, plans exist almost everywhere to expand as fast as possible. If the political situation permits, there is certainly enough Japanese expertise available at the present time to see that these plans are realizable.

It should also be appreciated that several of the largest copper producers have no choice but to continue copper production regardless of the price, since copper is their only crop, so to speak. Moreover in all these countries—and, for that matter, almost all the less developed countries—there is a great deal of room for the deflation of the *real* wage via inflation. Under the circumstances it is hardly proper to speak of a floor to the copper price.

At the same time it is apparent that when the price of copper goes over 50 cents, there is ample room for new capacity in the copper industry, even with the technology of 1970. Probably the best way to explain the investment programs under way at the present time is to recall that the price of copper moved above 50 cents quite soon after the landing of American troops in Vietnam, and for the most part stayed above this level until 1970. If, as may have happened, the leaders of the international copper industry have been able to convince themselves that the era of 30- and 40-cent copper is a thing of the past, then a great deal of new capacity can probably be justified. According to an estimate of the U.S. Department of the Interior, there is a sizable difference between the reserves recoverable at 50 cents per pound and those at 60 cents. Table 8–1 presents this estimate.

Sir Ronald Prain has supplied some data to the International Bank for Reconstruction and Development which shows capacity changes as a function

Table 8–1. Copper Reserves Recoverable at Various Prices
(Cents per Pound)*

	50 Cents	60 Cents	70 Cents	80 Cents
World	268	301	329	365
Centrally planned economies	42	43	45	48
World (excluding CPE's)	226	258	284	317
CIPEC (total)	107	122	138	156
Chile	54	62	69	76
Peru	14	19	24	29
Zambia	20	21	23	25
Zaire (Congo)	19	20	22	25
Non-CIPEC	119	136	146	161
U.S.	73	85	85	90

Source: U.S. Department of the Interior.
*In millions of tons.

of cost changes. These costs are average costs that can be taken as an approximation of long-run normal price, on the basis of which it can be postulated that production is determined. From this data Takeuchi has calculated some elasticities: "price" elasticity = percentage change in capacity divided by percentage change in costs (= percentage change in price).

The interpretation of this material is as follows. When the price falls from, say, 47.5 cents to 45 cents, world production should fall by about 12 percent—that is, 12 percent of capacity should go out of operation. The next step is for some enterprising graduate student to adjust these figures for the change in ownership patterns (= nationalizations) that have taken place in those years since these data were accumulated. For instance, it seems almost inconceivable to me that, at the present time, there could be a fall in production in the less developed of the producing countries within ranges down to 35 cents.

Similarly, some attention must be given to the attempts to influence price that will result from the formation of a negotiating organization such as CIPEC. If CIPEC could manage to function in a manner similar to OPEC (the oil producers' association) the "opinions" offered in the foregoing paragraphs would have to be drastically modified. Europe, in particular, would be in a particularly sensitive position. Of course, whether Europeans would be prepared to increase or even continue their development assistance in a situation where the price of copper and other raw materials doubled every two or three years is something we don't know just now—although that shouldn't keep us from thinking about it.

Table 8-2.   Price 'Elasticities' of Supply of Copper in Various Cost Ranges (1968)*

Cost Range Cents/Pound	Change in Cost (%)	Change in Capacity (%)	Elasticity
20.0–22.5	12.5	25.2	2.02
22.5–25.0	11.1	10.0	0.99
25.0–27.5	10.0	7.2	0.72
27.5–30.0	9.1	13.0	1.43
30.0–32.5	8.3	8.3	1.00
32.5–35.0	7.7	7.3	0.95
35.0–37.5	7.1	1.8	0.25
37.5–40.0	6.7	4.6	0.69
40.0–42.5	6.5	4.4	0.68
42.5–45.0	5.9	6.4	1.08
45.0–47.5	5.6	12.1	2.17
47.5–50.0	5.3	0	0

Source: Takeuchi 1972.

* World data, excluding centrally planned economies, are based on cost at mine plus cost of delivery to Europe.

Appendix A

The typical elementary textbook discussion of a commodity market is carried out in terms of a model of the following type:

(A)
$$S = f(p)$$
$$D = h(p)$$
$$S = D$$

S = Supply
D = Demand
p = price

This simple model is, of course, discussed employing the well-known diagram of the following type:

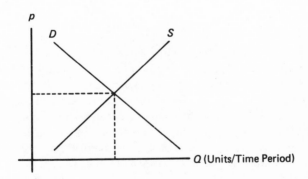

What the reader should observe is the way demand and supply are measured: we have both demand and supply in units per time period. With copper, for example, we would have tons per year.

Unfortunately, this kind of model will only answer a limited number of questions for us. Inventories, for example, do not enter explicitly into this model, and by now we are aware that inventories are quite prominent in any discussion of the copper market. As a matter of fact, they are crucial because of the role they play in price determination.

Price formation takes place in the U.S. in approximately the following way: First, producers decide what price they believe to be a long-run equilibrium price. On the basis of this price they make their production decision. The question now is, what happens to stocks? If the price is too low, demand is high and stocks fall. This depletion of inventories is the signal to producers that a higher price is in order, and adjustments take place until some sort of equilibrium is reached. A number of arguments exist that the U.S. producer price adjusts too slowly. (On this point the reader is referred to Chapter 6 of this book.)

A similar sort of phenomenon takes place outside the U.S. As noted often in this book, much pricing outside the U.S. is linked to the LME price during the period of delivery. If, for example, I sell x tons of copper today for delivery one year from now, most likely the price will be related to the LME price at that time. What this means is that I am selling at an unknown price, but that this price is related to actual supply-demand conditions at the time of delivery. This is true because the LME price reacts much faster than the U.S. producer price, adjusting in step with changes in stocks in LME warehouses. (The question of just where these stocks are being held does not seem to be important, as far as I can tell. Instead it is probably possible to say that the LME price adjusts with the changes in all producers' and consumers' stocks outside the U.S., and that stock changes inside the U.S. also probably have some bearing on the matter.)

The important thing that is being discussed here is that it is movement in stocks (in other words, inventories) that must be observed if we want to explain price movements, and not just the amount that producers and consumers are willing to put on or take off the market at a certain price. A large part of the present discussion can be shortened by saying that price changes in this market seem to be a function of the ratio of inventories to consumption, or the *change* in price is a function of the ratio of the change in inventories to the change in consumption, or some relationship of this nature. (A simpler formulation given below has the change in price as a linear function of the change in inventories.)

On the other hand, the demand for a good such as copper is largely determined by the level of industrial production or income. Copper is an intermediate input into many industrial and consumer goods, and there is a clear relationship, almost of an input-output nature, between the demand for these goods and the level of such aggregate indicators as production. The role of price, on the other hand, is ambiguous. On the basis of the simple flow demand curve shown earlier, increases in price mean decreases in demand. But evidence exists from Germany and Japan (and elsewhere) that when price increases are sharp and persistent, demand increases as a result of speculators buying in anticipation of further price increases. The reader will note that this type of buying ties in with the discussion in the above paragraph, since this speculative buying is for the most part a demand for inventories—that is, for inputs to be used in the productive process in a future period.

The simplest model for replacing (A) is then one of the following type:

$$
\text{(B)} \quad
\begin{aligned}
S &= f(p) \\
D &= h(Y, p) \\
\Delta p &= \alpha \Delta I \qquad \text{(or)} \qquad \Delta P = \beta \frac{\Delta I}{\Delta D} \\
D\text{--}S &= \Delta I
\end{aligned}
$$

Two possibilities are suggested for the price equation, but there are obviously many more. Even this model, however, places too much emphasis on flows, where flows are identified as variables that are measured in units per time period. The sort of model required to discuss this type of market properly is a so-called stock demand model where flows may of course be present, but the key variable is the stock of the commodity, and considerable attention is given the demand for this stock and the variables of which it is a function.

Readers who are interested in the theoretical aspects of stock and stock-flow models are referred to the work of Clower,[1] while econometric models employing price formation equations of the type given in (B) are to be found in Ertek [1967]; Fisher, Cootner, and Baily [1972]; and Banks [1971a].

---

[1] The basic paper is Clower [1954].

Appendix B

Two interesting and important papers by Bardhan and Lewis [1970] and Khang [1968] have taken the simple neoclassical model, augmented by an imported input obtained in return for an export good whose growth rate is exogenously determined, and used it to discuss some problems facing less developed countries dependent on international trade.

I believe that for pedagogical reasons this may someday be a useful model, and so I would like to simplify it somewhat by examining its equilibrium properties. The starting point is the production function $Q = K^{\alpha} M^{\beta} L^{\phi}$, where M is the imported input and $\phi = 1 - \alpha - \beta$. Taking the price of this input as numeraire, with P the price of domestic output (and thus also the terms of trade), we see immediately from the properties of this type of production function that the return to this input must be $1 \cdot M = \beta PQ$, which is equal to PX since trade is balanced.

$$\dot{M}/M = \dot{P}/P + \dot{Q}/Q = \dot{P}/P + \dot{X}/X \tag{1}$$

We also know that the equilibrium properties of the neoclassical model without technical change call for $\dot{Q}/Q = \dot{K}/K$, and so we have $\dot{Q}/Q = \dot{K}/K = \dot{X}/X$. If we now differentiate the production function and employ the above relations we get, with $L = 1 \cdot e^{ut}$ and $\dot{L}/L = u$:

$$\frac{\dot{X}(1-\alpha)}{X} \frac{}{\beta} = \frac{\dot{M}}{M} + \frac{\phi}{\beta} u \tag{2}$$

$$\frac{\dot{X}}{X} \frac{\phi}{\beta} = \frac{\dot{M}}{M} - \frac{\dot{X}}{X} + \frac{\phi}{\beta} u \tag{2'}$$

but we see from (1) that $\dot{M}/M - \dot{X}/X = \dot{P}/P$, so we have:

$$\frac{\dot{X}}{X}\frac{\phi}{\beta} = \frac{\dot{P}}{P} + \frac{\phi}{\beta}u \tag{3}$$

The demand relationship for exports can now be introduced. This is $X = P^n e^{\lambda t}$, where n is an elasticity (with $n < 0$), and λ is the exogenous rate of growth of exports. Differentiating this we get:

$$\frac{\dot{X}}{X} = n\frac{\dot{P}}{P} + \lambda \tag{4}$$

Putting this in (3) gives immediately:

$$\frac{\dot{P}}{P} = \frac{\phi(\lambda - u)}{\beta - n\phi} \tag{5}$$

It is now possible to get directly from (4) and our understanding of the long-run neoclassical equilibrium:

$$\frac{\dot{X}}{X} = \frac{\dot{K}}{K} = \frac{\dot{Q}}{Q} = \frac{\lambda\beta - n\phi u}{\beta - n\phi} \tag{6}$$

and from (1) and (6):

$$\frac{\dot{M}}{M} = \frac{(\phi + \beta) - u(\phi + \phi n)}{\beta - n\phi} \tag{7}$$

Some conclusions may now be drawn from the above. Since $\beta - n\phi > 0$ ($n < 0$) if $\lambda > u$ the terms of trade increase over time, and if $u > \lambda$ they decrease. Also we observe that the "weights" for λ and u in (6) sum to one, thus $\dot{Q}/Q$ (and $\dot{K}/K$ and $\dot{X}/X$) is larger than the smaller of λ or u, but smaller than the larger. What this means is that if $\lambda > u$ output per head increases, while the opposite is true if $u > \lambda$. A similar statement can be made about $\dot{V}/V$ in its relation to λ and u.

Although these results are not entirely unexpected, it is nice to be able to generate them from a model we know so much about. Moreover, by refining this model to a certain extent, Bardhan and Lewis suggest that a bridge can be built between the Oniki-Uzawa-type models and the Chenery-Strout two-gap analysis. The importance of such a synthesis is obvious.

Appendix C

I would like to use this appendix to solve a problem in capital allocation arising when situations arise that are typical of those described in the last section of this chapter. The problem has been examined in the simplified version considered here by Little [1961] and Seton [1960]. The object is to obtain their results without having to resort to their unwieldy mathematics.

The initial assumption is that we have an amount $\bar{K}$ of capital to begin with. One part will go as an input to the industrial sector, and this is called K_I; while the other is used to "transfer" workers into the industrial sector. This is K_c.

The expression transfer, as used here, means the following: if there is a cost of urbanization, if a worker must be trained before he can enter industrial employment, if he must be paid a wage differential before he will leave the "traditional" sector for the industrial sector, or if workers in the industrial sector require some special consumption good—for example, a good that must be imported or manufactured in the industrial sector—then even if there is "surplus" or "excess" labor in the economy, there is a *real cost* in transferring this labor into industrial service. The total amount of this cost, in capital goods, is K_c.

It should be observed that as stated, none of the initial capital is used as an input to produce the other components of consumption—the consumption of capital owners, nonproduction workers, etc. This could be called K_c', and thus initial capital could be divided as follows: $\bar{K} = K_c + \bar{K}_c' + K_I$. As customary in models of this type, the part that is regarded as "saved" is $K_I + K_c$. Similarly, there is another part of consumption that can be attributed to traditional capital—the nonshiftable capital that is to be found in the traditional sector. This consumption accrues to the occupants of the traditional sector and, to the extent that it can be transferred without cost, the industrial workers.

A special point that must be clarified, however, concerns the domestic production of capital goods. Both Little and Seton have this type of production explicitly in their models; however, this is obviously unnecessary as well as premature: there are very few of the less developed countries that have a substantial capital goods sector. In the case of a mining economy it is only necessary that output (of ore, smelter products, etc.) can be transformed into capital goods. Thus the inputs K_I and L_I shown below might be inputs in the mining sector that result in an output which, via foreign trade, is transformed into capital goods. This means that with economic growth we have $\overline{K}_t, \overline{K}_{t+1}, \overline{K}_{t+2}, \ldots$ as the amount of capital we have to allocate in periods $t, t+1, t+2 \ldots$ and so on, assuming that we have no consumption by capital owners, nonproduction workers, etc. Otherwise the amount that is to be allocated is $s\overline{K}_t, s\overline{K}_{t+1}, s\overline{K}_{t+2}, \ldots$ etc. If we now assume that there is a cost of w_c units of traditional goods for each unit of labor entering the industrial sector, and k_c units of capital is allocated to the traditional sector (which has a capital coefficient of v_c), it is obvious that the amount of labor that is transferred is $v_c K_c / w_c$. The following simple nonlinear program can then be formulated.[1]

$$\text{Max } F(K_I, L_I) = F\left(K_I, \frac{v_c K_c}{w_c}\right)$$

Subject to: $s\overline{K} = K_I + K_c$

and: $K_I, K_c \geqslant 0$

Since F is concave we get from the dual of this expression:

$$\lambda = \frac{\partial F}{\partial K_I} = \frac{v_c}{w_c} \frac{\partial F}{\partial L_I}$$

or: $$\frac{\partial F / \partial K_I}{\partial F / \partial L_I} = \frac{v_c}{w_c}$$

---

[1] As an example, take a case where an individual transferring to the industrial sector requires a wage differential before leaving the traditional sector (even if it is so that the wage he is receiving in the traditional sector can be transferred intact—for example, via taxation, altruism on the part of his relatives, etc.). Let this wage differential be equal to 20 units of food (i.e. the traditional 'good'), and so $w_c = 20$. If one unit of capital applied to the production of food gives 5 units of food ($v_c = 5$), then the real cost of a unit of labor in capital goods is 20/5 = 4 units of capital. Put another way, 100 units of capital allocated to the traditional sector can transfer 25 units of labor.

This is essentially the allocation rule derived by Little and Seton. The second order condition for a constrained maximum is also obviously satisfied. The reader can verify this immediately by examining the usual Hessian determinant, where we see that:

$$
\begin{vmatrix}
F_{11} & F_{12} & -1 \\
F_{21} & F_{22} & -1 \\
-1 & -1 & 0
\end{vmatrix} > 0
$$

It can be observed, however, that $F(K_I, L_I)$ can be written $G(K_I, K_C)$, and thus we also get from the dual:

$$
\frac{\partial G/\partial K_I}{\partial G/\partial K_c} = 1
$$

Since an increase in the output of the industrial sector is possible through an increase in K_I or L_I —with L_I resulting from a transformation of K_c —we see that at the optimum capital is allocated in such a manner that the marginal unit will provide an equal increment of industrial goods, regardless of the sector to which it is sent. What this means in terms of the discussion earlier in this chapter is that under certain circumstances more attention will have to be paid to increasing the supply of labor through decreasing the transfer cost. What this means is either operating directly on the wage or, since this is often impossible, operating directly on the productivity of the agricultural sector.

Appendix D

In this appendix we will examine an aspect of input selection from the production theoretical point of view. The usual optimization theory presentation works as follows: a cost function is to be minimized in the presence of a given production function and given output. As for the production function, it contains all possible inputs. For example, with X_c and X_a inputs of copper and aluminum, and with other conceivable inputs we have:

$$\text{Min} \quad \phi(X_c, X_a, \ldots, X_i, \ldots)$$

With: $\qquad (X_c, X_a, \ldots, X_i, \ldots) \geqslant 0$

And: $\qquad X_c, X_a, \ldots, X_i, \ldots \geqslant 0$

If we take the situation with, e.g., a transmission line, it happens to be the case that we would not normally expect copper and aluminum to appear in the same production function. We do not use so much copper and so much aluminum—we use copper *or* aluminum (except in the relatively new composite cables, for which neither the conventional analysis nor the one given below is correct). As for the correct production function, it should take the form $g(X_1, X, \overline{q}) = 0$, where X is copper *or* aluminum cable size, X_1 is electrical input in kilowatt-hours and $\overline{q}$ is electrical output in kilowatt hours, which is taken as given.[1]

---

[1] The standard references here are Ballinger [1952] and Knowlton [1949].

It should also be specified that $M \geqq X$ and $X \geqq m$, where here we have the upper and lower bounds on the size of the cable. These last constraints are of more than theoretical consideration, since in the design of transmission lines, it is always necessary to consider the swinging of the cable, and the size and strength of connections and insulators. The cost function in the example given here will be linear, but as the reader is probably aware, nonlinearity in this function would not complicate matters a great deal. This cost function is:

$$\text{Min } C = \phi(X_1, X_c, X_a) = w_1 X_1 + w_c X_c + w_a X_a$$

(with)

λ_1 :	$g_1(X_1, X_c, \bar{q}) \geqq 0$		output at least $\bar{q}$
λ_2 :	$g_2(X_1, X_a, \bar{q}) \geqq 0$		output at least $\bar{q}$
λ_3 :	$g_3(X_c, X_a) = -X_c + M_c \geqq 0$		size no greater than M_c
λ_4 :	$g_4(X_c, X_a) = -X_a + M_a \geqq 0$		size no greater than M_a
λ_5 :	$g_5(X_c, X_a) = X_c - m_c \geqq 0$		size no less than m_c
λ_6 :	$g_6(X_c, X_a) = X_a - m_a \geqq 0$		size no less than m_a

$$X_1, X_a, X_c \geqq 0$$

If we now write the dual of the above we get:

$$w_1 - \sum_{i=1}^{6} \lambda_i \frac{\partial g_i}{\partial X_i} \geqq 0$$

$$w_c - \sum_{i=1}^{6} \lambda_i \frac{\partial g_i}{\partial X_c} \geqq 0$$

$$w_a - \sum_{i=1}^{6} \lambda_i \frac{\partial g_i}{\partial X_a} \geqq 0$$

if: $\quad w_1 - \lambda_1 \dfrac{\partial g_1}{\partial X_1} - \lambda_2 \dfrac{\partial g_2}{\partial X_2} > 0$, then $X_1 = X_1\,(X,\,q) = \text{Min}$

if: $\quad w_c - \lambda_1 \dfrac{\partial g_1}{\partial X_c} - \lambda_3\,(-1) - \lambda_5\,(1) > 0$, then $X_c = m_c$

if: $\quad w_a - \lambda_2 \dfrac{\partial g_2}{\partial X_2} - \lambda_4\,(-1) - \lambda_6\,(1) > 0$, then $X_a = m_a$

If we assume that the functions g_1 and g_2 are concave, then $X_1 = X_1\,(M_c,\,\bar{q}\,)$ or $X_1 = X_1\,(M_a,\,\bar{q}\,)$. From the above we know that for a neoclassical interior solution we have $g_1\,(X_1,\,X_c,\,\bar{q}\,) = 0,\,\lambda_1 > 0$, $g_3\,(\ ) > 0,\,\lambda_3 = 0,\,g_5\,(\ ) > 0,\,\lambda_5 = 0;\quad g_2\,(X_1,\,Xa,\,\bar{g}\,) = 0,\,\lambda_2 > 0,\,g_4\,(\ ) > 0,\,\lambda_4 = 0,\,g_6\,(\ ) > 0,\,\lambda_6 = 0$. For one of the four possible boundary solutions we would have $g_1\,(\ ) = 0,\,\lambda_1 > 0,\,g_3 = 0,\,\lambda_3 > 0,\,g_5\,(\ ) > 0,\,\lambda_5 = 0$, and so on.

Appendix E

The purpose of this appendix is to give the reader who is interested in the copper industry some references that will facilitate his reading.

Once the reader has gone through the first two chapters of this book, he would probably be interested in the study prepared for UNCTAD by Bottelier [1968]. Also quite general but important are the papers by Stewardson [1970] and Treadgold [1971]. Treadgold looks at the cost of mining in a very underdeveloped country, and does so in a way most readers should have no trouble following. Another fairly general paper is Somerset's [n.d.].

Papers with a substantial polemic content are those of Brundenius [1972] and Girvan [n.d.]. Brundenius' article is quite well written and contains interesting diagrams and figures.

Material on scrap is not easy to come by. A UNIDO document by Spendlove [1969] was very informative for me. Other papers on scrap are to be found in a special issue of the *Metal Bulletin,* May 1965, in particular H. Grillo's "The Importance of Scrap." I understand that a recent study done for CIPEC by the Batelle Institute in Geneva devotes some attention to scrap. Unfortunately this study is classified, but perhaps part of it will surface someday.

A more routine presentation of the copper industry is the book by Herfindahl [1959]. In the same vein is an unpublished UNCTAD memorandum by Chambers and Ashton [1967]. For readers interested in the spectral properties of copper prices, the paper by Labys, Rees, and Elliot [1971], contains much useful information.

Policy questions concerned with the less developed countries are taken up in the study by Bottelier mentioned earlier, and also a short book by Bohm [1968]. One of the most important documents along this line is the report to the Zambian Government by John Mars. I am unable to say, however, just how the reader will obtain a copy of this important document, since as far as I know it is not in general circulation. Much more attainable is the study by Baldwin [1966] which deals with Zambia, and, of course, the paper by Takeuchi [1972].

All economists interested in metals should read the *Engineering and Mining Journal,* which is a monthly based in New York. Among other things it contains plans for capacity expansion, the most detailed price information, cost studies, and all sorts of useful odds and ends. Another indispensible source is the *London Financial Times,* which is published six times a week. Another valuable reference is *Metals Week.* UNIDO has occasional conferences that produce interesting papers—I mentioned two of these earlier—and CIPEC produces a quarterly report and recently issued a volume consisting largely of statistical material (with comments). UNCTAD has a yearly commodity survey with a section on copper and also produces a monthly bulletin of commodity prices.

Last but not least, anyone reading this book realizes the part played in it by the statistical sources: in particular, the *World Metal Statistics* of the World Bureau of Metal Statistics, *Metal Statistics* of Metallgesellschaft A.G. (Frankfurt), and the *International Wrought Copper Council Statistical Reports.*

References

Alexander, W.O. 1967. The competition of metals. *Scientific American.*

Arrow, K.J. 1962. The economic implications of learning by doing. *Review of Economic Studies* 80. 155–73.

Arrow, K.J. 1967. Applications of control theory to economic growth. Mimeographed report, Stanford University.

Baldwin, P.E. 1966. *Economic development and export growth.* Berkeley: University of California Press.

Banks, Ferdinand E. 1971. An econometric note on the demand for refined zinc. *Zeitschrift für Nationalökonomi* 31:443–452. (a)

Banks, Ferdinand E. 1971. The economics of exhaustible resources: a note. *Ekonomiska Samfundets Tidskrift* (b) 24:259–262.

Banks, Ferdinand E. 1972. An econometric model of the world tin economy: a comment. *Econometrica* 40:749–752.

Bardhan, P., and Lewis, Sydney. 1970. Models of growth with imported inputs. *Economica* (New Series):37 373–385.

Bohm, Peter. 1968. *The pricing of copper in international trade.* Stockholm: Economic Research Institute, Stockholm School of Economics.

Bottelier, J.C. 1968. A case study of the world copper industry. Study prepared for UNCTAD.

Bradley, P.G. 1967. *The economics of crude petroleum production.* Amsterdam: North Holland Publishing Company.

Brundenius, Claes. 1972. The anatomy of imperialism: multinational mining corporations in Peru. *Journal of Peace Research* 3:189–207

Bullinger, C.E. 1952. *Engineering economic analysis.* New York: McGraw-Hill.

Chambers, Brian, and Ashton, John. 1967. The longer term outlook for nonferrous metals exports from the developing countries. Unpublished UNCTAD memorandum.

Clower, R.W. 1954. An investigation into the dynamics of investment. *American Economic Review* 44:69–77.

Desai, Meghnad. 1972. An econometric model of the world tin economy: a reply to Mr. Banks. *Econometrica* 40:753–755.

Ertek, Tumay. 1967. The world demand for copper, 1948–63: an econometric study. Ph. D. dissertation, Wisconsin University.

Fisher, F.M., Cootner, P.H., and Baily, M.N. 1972. An econometric model of the world copper industry. *Bell Journal of Economics and Management Science* 3:568–609.

Girvan, Norman. 1970 n.d. Copper in Chile: a study in conflict between corporate and national economy. Ph.D. dissertation, University of the West Indies.

Gordon, R.L. 1967. A reinterpretation of the pure theory of exhaustion. *Journal of Political Economy* 75:274–286.

Grillo, H. 1965. The importance of scrap. *The Metal Bulletin,* Special Issue on Copper.

Herfindahl, O.C. 1959. *Copper costs and prices: 1879–1957.* Baltimore: Johns Hopkins Press.

Houthakker, Henrik S. 1970. Copper: the anatomy of a malfunctioning market. Lecture presented at Duke University, March 1970.

Houthakker, Henrik S., and Taylor, L.D. 1966. *Consumer demand in the United States, 1929–1970.* Cambridge: Harvard University Press.

Keyck, L.M. 1954. *Distributed lags and investment analysis.* Amsterdam: North Holland Publishing Company.

Khang, C. 1968. A neoclassical growth model of a resource poor open economy. *International Economic Review* 9:329–338.

Knowlton, A.E. 1949. *Standard handbook for electrical engineers.* New York: McGraw-Hill.

Labys, W.C., Rees, H.J.B., and Elliott, C.M. 1971. Copper price behavior and the London Metal Exchange. *Applied Economics* 3:99–113.

Little, I.M.D. 1961. The real cost of labour, and the choice between consumption and investment. *Quarterly Journal of Economics* 75:1–14.

Lundberg, E. 1962. *Produktivitet och Räntabilitet.* Stockholm P.A. Norstedt och Söner.

Nerlove, M. 1958. *The dynamics of supply: estimation of farmers' response to price.* Baltimore: Johns Hopkins Press.

Newhouse, Joseph P., and Sloan, Frank A. 1966. An econometric study of copper supply. Unpublished report, Rand Corporation.

Seton, F. 1960. Industrialization in overpopulated areas, a geometric interpretation of certain aspects. *Oxford Economic Papers.* 12:202–214.

Somerset, G.S. 1970 n.d. Economic aspects of copper production and marketing possibilities for developing countries. UNIDO, ID/WG/74/4.

Spendlove, Max J. 1969. Opportunities in the production of secondary non-ferrous metals. *UNIDO,* 4 September, 1969.

Stewardson, B.R. 1970. The nature of competition in the world market for refined copper. *The Economic Record.* 46:169–181.

Takeuchi, Kenji. 1972. CIPEC and the copper export earnings of member countries. *The Developing Economies.* 4:1–29.

Tilton, S.E. 1966. The choice of trading partners: an analysis of international trade in aluminum, bauxite, copper, lead manganese, tin, and zinc. Ph.D. dissertation, Yale University.

Treadgold, M.L. 1971. Bougainville copper and the economic development of Papua-New Guinea. *The Economic Record.* 47:186–202.

Wallis, Kenneth F. 1972. *Introductory econometrics.* London: Gray-Mills Publishing Ltd.

Witherell, W. 1967. An econometric model of the world wool market. Ph.D. dissertation, Princeton University.

Index

About the Author

Ferdinand E. Banks attended Illinois Institute of Technology and Roosevelt University (Chicago, Illinois), graduating with a B.A. in Economics. After military service in the Orient and Europe, he worked as an engineer and systems and procedures analyst. His graduate work was done at the University of Stockholm, from which he received the M.Sc. and Fil. Lic. (Ph.D) in Economics. He taught for five years at the University of Stockholm; was Senior Lecturer in Economics and Statistics at the United Nations African Institute for Economic and Development Planning, Dakar, Senegal; and has been consultant lecturer in macroeconomics for the OECD in Lisbon, Portugal. From 1968 until 1971 he was an econometrician for the United Nations Commission on Trade and Development in Geneva, Switzerland. At present he is associate professor and research fellow at the University of Uppsala, Sweden.